W9-CZG-047

THE NEW EDUCATIONAL MUSIC COURSE

FOURTH MUSIC READER

BY

JAMES M. McLAUGHLIN

DIRECTOR OF MUSIC, BOSTON PUBLIC SCHOOLS, AUTHOR OF "ELEMENTS AND NOTATION OF MUSIC"

AND

W. W. GILCHRIST

VOCAL TEACHER AND CONDUCTOR, COMPOSER OF "SONGS FOR CHILDREN" ART SONGS, CANTATAS, ORCHESTRAL WORKS

GINN & COMPANY

BOSTON · NEW YORK · CHICAGO · LONDON

612.11

The Athenæum Press
GINN & COMPANY · PROPRIETORS · BOSTON · U.S.A.

INTRODUCTION

The place of the Fourth Music Reader in this system of musical instruction will be better understood by a brief survey of the entire Course.

The Aim. The aim of the New Educational Music Course is:

The New Educational Music Course

To inspire love of good music;
To develop a musical voice;
To teach sight singing;
To induce musical interpretation.

The Material. *A distinguishing feature* of the material throughout the Course is that each number illustrates some well-known characteristic of music, racial or individual, and contains that vital quality called *musical content*, which appeals to the inexperienced learner as well as to the trained musician.

Basis of choice. Aside from the elements in notation of music, which are noted as they occur in the Course, there has been in the choice of material a constant recognition of the ideal development of the pupil. This includes the physical development resulting from deep breathing, the intellectual development involved in a systematic study of the subject, and the subtle development of character which comes from familiarity with good music.

All forms of music are represented, from the simple folk song to the melodies of the greatest composers of all nationalities, gleaned from the fields of song, cantata, oratorio, opera, and symphony.

Some of the *best living composers* are represented by settings of "poems every child should know."

The *wide range of song subjects* and the variety of moods represented in the Course respond to the complex nature and environment of youth.

The *part songs* are made particularly attractive by contrapuntal treatment, by the introduction of the melodic theme in the lower voices, and by voice accompaniments.

The *vocal arrangements* from the classics reflect the spirit of the original, both melodically and harmonically.

The Plan. The plan underlying the arrangement of the material furnishes *an outline for consecutive study;* at the same time the material is so grouped that any modification of the plan may easily be made by teachers when desirable.

Suggestive headings and marginal notes make clear the special rhythmic and melodic problems in process of development. The marginal notes accompany the melodies which first incorporate the problems named.

The Glossary in each reader is an authority upon which teacher and pupil can depend for definition and representation of musical terms and signs occurring in that reader. At the same time it summarizes for the teacher the technical work which study of the reader develops. The glossaries of the successive books contain such analysis as may logically be presented in connection with the respective readers.

The Fourth Music Reader is adapted for study in the average seventh or combined seventh and eighth grades.

The Fourth Music Reader

Part I of the Fourth Music Reader is a review of the problems of the Third Music Reader and the introduction of a skip before and after the intermediate tone.

Part II completes the circle of major keys.

Part III places the major and minor modes in relation to each other.

Part IV is a collection of duets, trios, part songs, and choruses for unchanged voices.

Part V introduces the bass clef.

As a rule Part V probably would not be used except in the combined grades suggested above, or where changed voices first appear. The range of the bass is such, however, that unchanged voices will find little or no difficulty in singing from the bass staff, if teachers wish to provide practice for all voices in reading from that staff.

Throughout the New Educational Music Course musical effect has preceded study of the reason for that effect. Up to this time the effect of using *six* of the major scale as the *tonic* has been experienced many times; but special study of the minor mode in contrast with the major mode has been deferred to this music reader.

Broad musical development. Recognition of musical effects through the sense of hearing, and reproduction of the same, should continue in every grade.

Suggestions

Melodic and rhythmic drill, attention to voice quality, pronunciation and articulation, and faithful interpretation of the sentiment expressed by the composer make the æsthetic and educational value of the music hour worthy of its place in the school program.

Assignment to parts. Voices should be grouped according to quality and range, and assigned to their proper parts. Frequent exchange of parts is advisable, however, so long as the voices are adapted to such exchange.

The probable range of voices at this period is first soprano, $\bar{c}$ to $\bar{\bar{g}}$; second soprano, $\bar{c}$ to $\bar{\bar{d}}$; alto, g to $\bar{b}$. Whenever the extremes of range are touched in the melodies of the Course, the approach is such as to induce the proper voice quality without effort or strain.

Written work. Individual progress may be tested, and the weak pupil strengthened, by requiring written reproduction of musical phrases or entire melodies sung or dictated. Where an instrument is available, written reproduction of one part, when two or more parts are being played, cultivates musical perception.

Song repertoire. The many songs worthy to be committed to memory, and the variety of song programs available within the music reader, merit special attention. The grouping of songs which represent the same musical forms adds interest and value to their study; thus, group selections from comic opera, pages 2, 16, 30, 54; from the symphony, pages 4, 27, 61; from oratorio, pages 96 and 111, etc., etc.

Acknowledgment

Acknowledgment is due to Messrs. Houghton, Mifflin & Co. for the use of "Angel of Peace" and "Omnipresence" by Oliver Wendell Holmes, "Stars of the Summer Night" by Henry W. Longfellow, and "Hymn of Thanksgiving" by John G. Whittier; and to the Right Reverend W C. Doane for the use of "Morning Hymn of Praise."

TABLE OF CONTENTS

PART I

REVIEW OF PRINCIPLES DEVELOPED IN PRECEDING READERS. INTERMEDIATE TONES APPROACHED AND FOLLOWED BY SKIPS

	PAGES
Key of C	1–3
Key of G	4–6
Key of F	7–9
Key of D	10–12
Key of B♭	13–15
Key of A	16–18
Key of E♭	19–21
Key of E	22–24
Key of A♭	25–27

PART II

CIRCLE OF KEYS COMPLETED

	PAGES
Keys of B, D♭, F♯, G♭, C♯, C♭	28–35

PART III

THE MINOR MODE IN CONTRAST WITH THE MAJOR MODE

	PAGES
Keys of C major and A minor	36–38
Keys of G major and E minor	39–41
Keys of F major and D minor	42–44
Keys of D major and B minor	45–47

PART III — *Continued*

	PAGES
Keys of B♭ major and G minor	48–50
Keys of A major and F♯ minor	51–53
Keys of E♭ major and C minor	54–56
Keys of E major and C♯ minor	57–59
Keys of A♭ major and F minor	60–62
Keys of B major and G♯ minor D♭ major and B♭ minor F♯ major and D♯ minor G♭ major and E♭ minor C♯ major and A♯ minor A♭ minor	63–67

PART IV

SONGS FOR UNCHANGED VOICES

	PAGES
Duets, trios, part songs, and choruses	68–127

PART V

THE F CLEF

Exercises, part songs, and choruses, arranged for three unchanged voices, or for two unchanged voices and bass voice	128–144
Patriotic Songs	144–149
Glossary	150–157
Terms and Signs of Expression	158
Index to Glossary	159–160
Index to Songs	161–162

Part I

REVIEW OF PRINCIPLES DEVELOPED IN PRECEDING READERS; INTERMEDIATE TONES APPROACHED AND FOLLOWED BY SKIPS

Legato
mp
mp
1
Andantino
mp
mp
2
HOMEWARD BOUND
Louis C. Elson
Harvey Worthington Loomis
Allegro
mf
3
1. Now the wind is blow - ing free, Ev - 'ry sail is spread,
2. Light - ly as a bird on wing, Sail we o'er the sea;
mf
1. Winds are blow - ing free And ev - 'ry sail is spread,
2. Light as bird on wing We sail a - cross the sea;
Foam - ing wake a - stern we see, Roll - ing waves a - head.
From the prow the spray we fling; Home-ward bound are we.
Foam - ing wake a - stern we see, Roll - ing waves a - head.
From the prow the spray we fling; Home-ward bound are we.

AUTUMN WOODS

NIXON WATERMAN

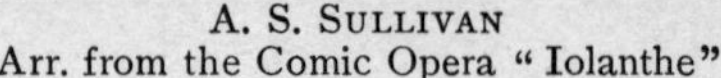
A. S. SULLIVAN
Arr. from the Comic Opera "Iolanthe"

4

Allegretto

mf

1. When skies are bright and fields are brown And au - tumn leaves come drift-ing down, A girl or boy can find true joy In ev - 'ry wood-land way. Then all the stur - dy for - est trees Be - stow their gifts with ev-'ry breeze, In nut - ting time the world's in rhyme And life's a gold-en day.

2. In bright Oc - to - ber's spark-ling air The rus - set land is strange-ly fair, And ev - 'ry way our feet may stray We fol - low pleas-ure's call. We love the spring with smil-ing face, We love the sum-mer's mel-low grace, But autumn's store of fun ga - lore Still seems the best of all.

(Lower part: ev - 'ry, ev - 'ry wood-land way. / fol - low, fol - low pleas-ure's call.)

f *mf*

Flat-six

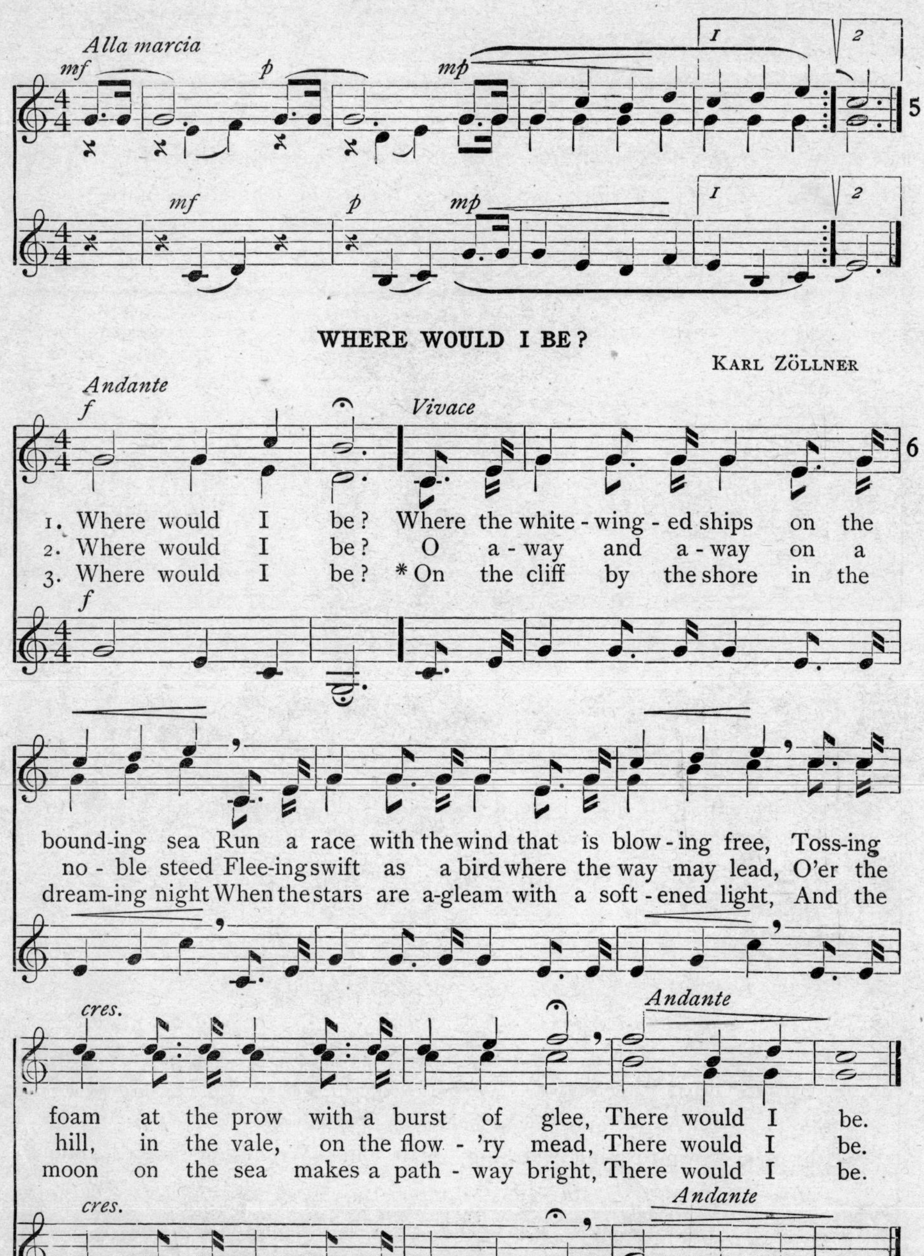
Alla marcia
mf
p
mp
1
2
5
WHERE WOULD I BE?
Karl Zöllner
Andante
f
Vivace
6
1. Where would I be? Where the white-wing-ed ships on the bounding sea Run a race with the wind that is blow-ing free, Toss-ing foam at the prow with a burst of glee, There would I be.
2. Where would I be? O a-way and a-way on a no-ble steed Flee-ing swift as a bird where the way may lead, O'er the hill, in the vale, on the flow-'ry mead, There would I be.
3. Where would I be? * On the cliff by the shore in the dream-ing night When the stars are a-gleam with a soft-ened light, And the moon on the sea makes a path-way bright, There would I be.
cres.
Andante

* From this point this stanza should be sung *andante piano*.

SONG OF THE WATERS

NATHAN HASKELL DOLE

HAYDN
Arr. from Symphony No. 14, Presto

7

Vivace
mp
cres - - - - - - - cen - - - - - - do
1. We hap - py - heart - ed wa - ters, The clouds' un - count - ed
2. We fill the lim - pid foun - tains On high and mist - y
dim - - - - - - - in - - - - u - - - -
daugh - ters, Ex - ult in song and laugh - ter While far - ing
moun - tains, Where might - y storms up - sweep - ing Break sum - mer's
en - - do cres - - - - - cen - - - - - do
through the earth! Our life is end - less mo - tion From o - cean back to
parch-ing drought. Then o - ver fal - len boul - ders, Round mas-sive gran - ite
dim - - - in - - - u - - en - - do
o - cean, But work and joy come aft - er Each new re - birth!
shoul - ders, Down-rush-ing, whirl-ing, leap - ing, We sing and shout.

THE DEWY DELL

Alfred Waymark. Adapted
Henry Smart
Allegretto
p
8
1. Down to the glist-'ning dew - y dell Where the perfumed vio-lets spring, And
2. Down in the qui - et, grass-y dell In a sha - dy, cool re - treat, We
p
1. Down to the glist - 'ning dew - y dell Where the per - fumed vio - lets spring, And
2. Down in the qui - et, grass - y dell In a sha - dy, cool re - treat, We
ev - 'ry ten - der flow - 'ry bell Bends 'neath the zeph-yr's wing, We will
hap - py fair - ies love to dwell Where rip - pling wa - ters meet, For they
ev - 'ry ten - der flow - 'ry bell Bends 'neath zeph - yr's wing, . .
hap - py fair - ies love to dwell Where clear wa - ters meet, . .
Sharp-four
haste from a - far, when the first bright star Beams on
sing us a ten - der, ca - ress - ing lay While we
We will haste when the first bright star Beams like a gem on
For they sing us a ten - der lay While on the moss we
Sharp-five
high, And the pale moon mounts her car To float thro' the placid sky.
rest, Where the zephyrs round us play Or sleep in the li - ly's breast.
high, And the pale moon mounts her car To float thro' the pla - cid, pla - cid sky.
rest, Where the zeph-yrs round us play Or sleep in the li - ly's, li - ly's breast.

Andante
mp
mf
9
mf
mp

OMNIPRESENCE

Hursley

Oliver Wendell Holmes — Peter Ritter

Andante

mf

10

1. Lord of all be - ing, throned a - far, Thy glo - ry
2. Sun of our life, Thy quick - 'ning ray Sheds on our
3. Grant us Thy truth to make us free, Hearts that will

flames from sun . . and star; Cen - ter and soul . of
path the glow . . of day; Star of our hope, Thy
burn with love . . for Thee, Till all Thy liv - ing

ev - 'ry sphere, Yet to each lov - ing heart how near!
soft - ened light Cheers the long watch - es of the night.
al - tars claim One ho - ly light, one heav'n - ly flame!

f

THE WEATHER VANE

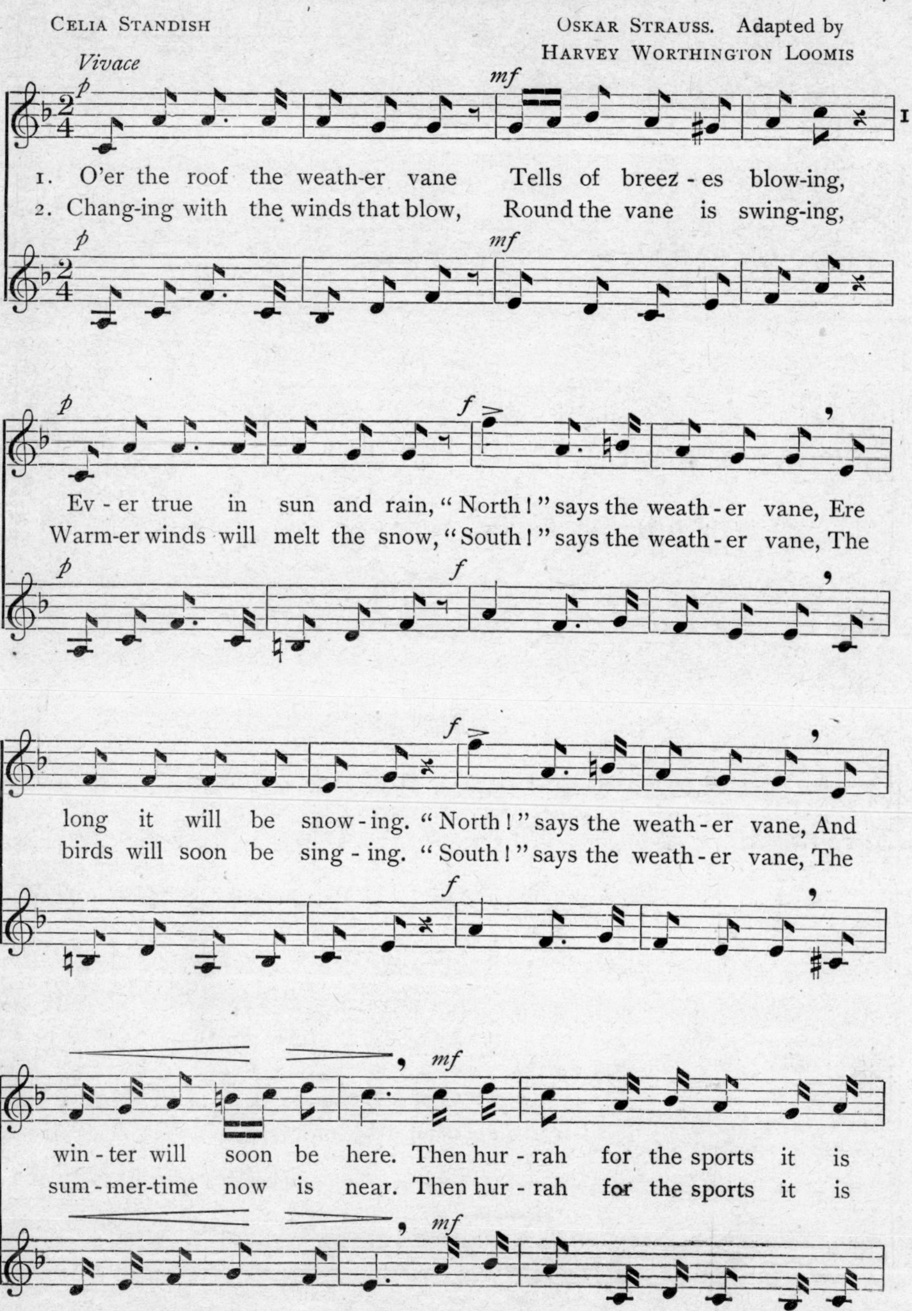
Celia Standish
Oskar Strauss. Adapted by
Harvey Worthington Loomis
Vivace
1. O'er the roof the weath-er vane Tells of breez - es blow-ing,
2. Chang-ing with the winds that blow, Round the vane is swing-ing,
Ev - er true in sun and rain, "North!" says the weath - er vane, Ere
Warm-er winds will melt the snow, "South!" says the weath - er vane, The
long it will be snow - ing. "North!" says the weath - er vane, And
birds will soon be sing - ing. "South!" says the weath - er vane, The
win - ter will soon be here. Then hur - rah for the sports it is
sum - mer-time now is near. Then hur - rah for the sports it is

bring - ing, For the ice and the snow,
bring - ing, To the fields we will go,
mf
bring - ing, bring - ing, Ho for the ice and snow, Though the
bring - ing, bring - ing, Then to the fields we'll go, Through the
mp
Ah, ah, ... ho -
Ah, ah, ... ho -
cold out of doors may be sting - ing, Nev - er mind, let the north wind
woods will the shouts be a - ring - ing, Then hur - rah ! let the south wind
mf
ho ! Hil - ly ho ! Hil - ly ho ! Let us
ho ! Hil - ly ho ! Hil - ly ho ! Let us
mf
blow ! . Ho, hil - ly ho ! Ho, hil - ly ho !
blow ! . Ho, hil - ly ho ! Ho, hil - ly ho !
cres.
a tempo
mf
wel - come Win - ter's reign, . For the coast - ing and skat - ing are
wel - come Sum-mer's reign, . For the fish - ing and sail - ing are
rit.
a tempo
cres.
mp
Wel - come Win - ter's reign, Ah, ah, ...
Wel - come Sum - mer's reign, Ah, ah, ...

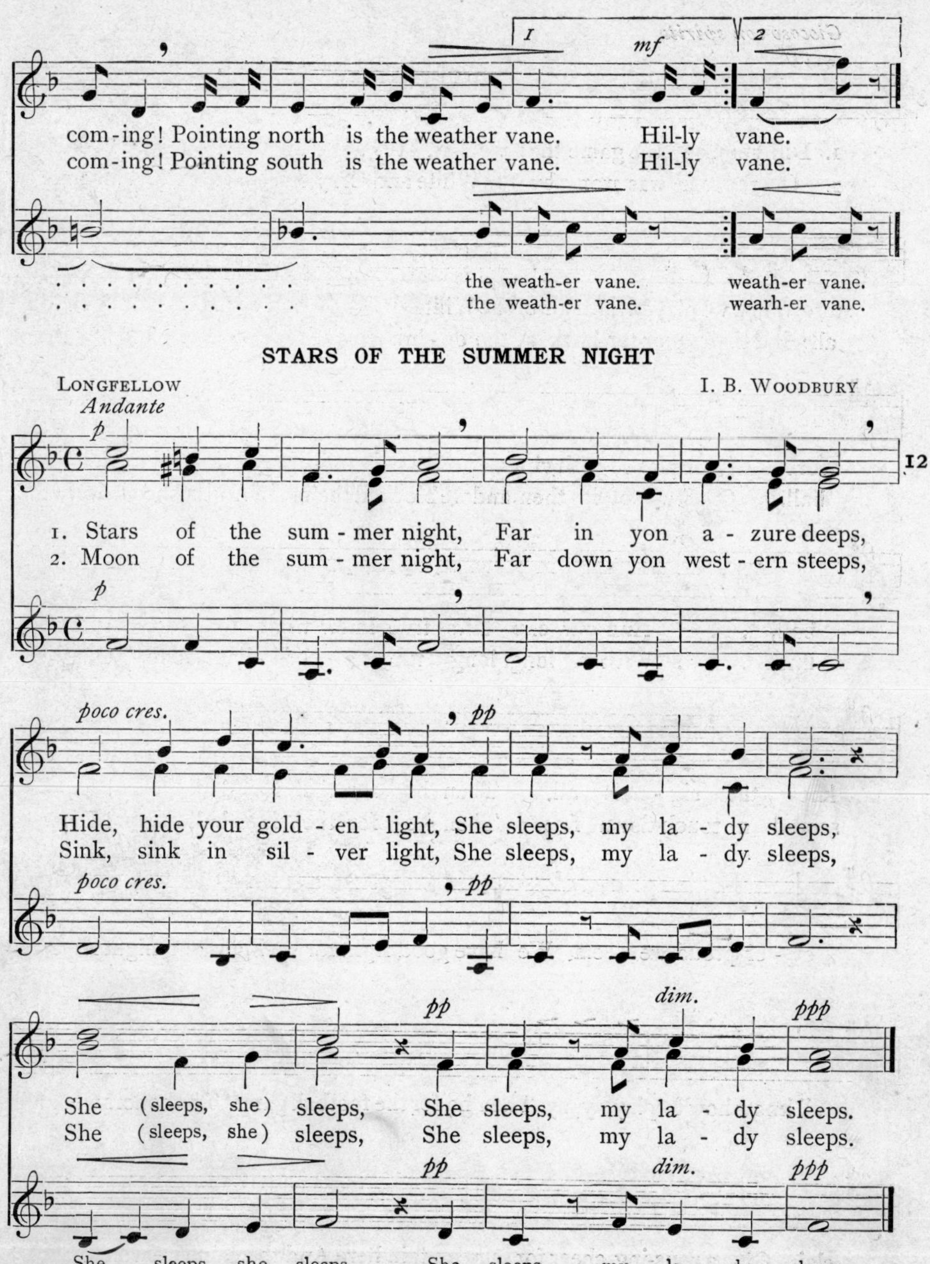
1
2
mf
com-ing! Pointing north is the weather vane. Hil-ly vane.
com-ing! Pointing south is the weather vane. Hil-ly vane.
. . . . the weath-er vane. weath-er vane.
. . . . the weath-er vane. wearh-er vane.
STARS OF THE SUMMER NIGHT
LONGFELLOW
I. B. WOODBURY
Andante
p
12
1. Stars of the sum - mer night, Far in yon a - zure deeps,
2. Moon of the sum - mer night, Far down yon west - ern steeps,
p
poco cres.
pp
Hide, hide your gold - en light, She sleeps, my la - dy sleeps,
Sink, sink in sil - ver light, She sleeps, my la - dy sleeps,
poco cres.
pp
pp
dim.
ppp
She (sleeps, she) sleeps, She sleeps, my la - dy sleeps.
She (sleeps, she) sleeps, She sleeps, my la - dy sleeps.
pp
dim.
ppp
She sleeps, she sleeps, She sleeps, my la - dy sleeps.
She sleeps, she sleeps, She sleeps, my la - dy sleeps.

A FOOT-BALL SONG

English Folk Tune

Giocoso con spirito

13

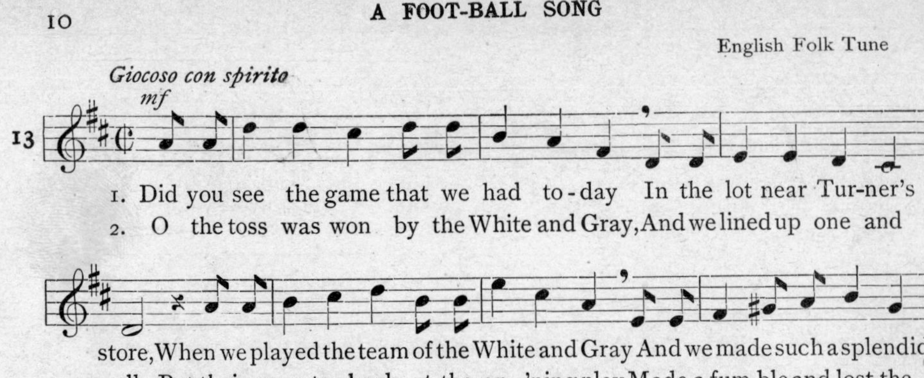

1. Did you see the game that we had to-day In the lot near Tur-ner's
2. O the toss was won by the White and Gray, And we lined up one and

store, When we played the team of the White and Gray And we made such a splendid
all; But their quar-ter back at the op-'ning play Made a fum-ble and lost the

score? O we played with vim, we were in good trim And longed to kick the
ball. O we kept it then, and we blocked their men And rushed it down the

ball, . . . And our cap-tain true knew what to do, And we
line, . . . With a long, long run, a bril-liant one, O we

knew the sig-nals all. Then ho for the foot-ball team! How-
scored a touch-down fine. Then ho for the foot-ball team! How-

ev-er proud we seem. We have good right for we know our might And we

all know how to play, ay, ay; Then ho for the football game! The honors we shall

claim. Give a rous-ing cheer for our cap-tain here And the game we won to-day.

WIND IN THE TREES

NIXON WATERMAN — M. LANSEN

Andantino grazioso
p
14
1. Through the tree - tops gen - tly sway - ing, Soft and low the wind a -
Through the tree - tops gen - tly sway - ing, Soft and low the wind a -
2. Like a mem - 'ry dim and haunt-ing, Is the song the wind is
Like a mem - 'ry dim and haunt - ing, Is the song the wind is
Sharp-four
stray - ing, In the branches paus - es to gen-tly swing the birds that
stray - ing, In the branch - es he stays to swing The birds that
chant - ing, In the oak-tree's branch - es, so broad, so high, That lift them-
chant - ing, In the branch - es of oak so high, That lift them-
dim.
p
sempre p
sweet - ly, mer - ri - ly chirp and sing. . And
sweet - ly, mer - ri - ly chirp and sing, that chirp and sing. And
selves so lov - ing - ly toward the sky. . . . Then
selves so lov - ing - ly toward the sky, the sky. Then through the
through the star-lit night he mur-murs till the day Greets the ro-sy east and
through the night he mur - murs till the day Greets the east and
through the pen-sive chant, a light - er, bright-er lay Breathes the frolic wind and
chant, the chant a light - er, bright - er lay Breathes the wind and
cres.
1.2. then he steals a - way, a - way. . . . . . . In his
then he steals a - way, a - way, He steals a - way. In his
p
play, . . and then he steals a - way, ...
play, his play, and then he steals a - way, He steals a - way, a -

p
p
gen - tly steals a - way, a - way, ...
way, ... a - way, He steals a - way, a -
rit. . . . .
p
pp
ppp
gen - tly steals a - way, a - way, a - way, a - way.
way, ... a - way, a - way, a - way, a - way.
MORNING HYMN OF PRAISE
WILLIAM C. DOANE
Ancient of Days
J. ALBERT JEFFERY
Maestoso
mf
15
1. An - cient of Days, who sit - test throned in glo - ry,
2. O Lord our God, with heart and voice a - dor - ing,
mf
To Thee all knees are bent, all voi - ces pray; Thy love has blest the
Praise we the good - ness that doth crown our days; Pray we that Thou wilt
wide world's wondrous story With light and life since E - den's dawning day.
hear us, still im - plor-ing Thy love and fa - vor, kept to us al - ways.

THE LIGHT-HEARTED FAIRY

Anonymous
C. B. Edmunds
Giocoso
mp
16
1. O who is so mer - ry, heigh ho! As the
2. O who is so mer - ry, heigh ho! As the
3. O who is so mer - ry, heigh ho! As the
heigh ho!
mf
light heart - ed fair - y, heigh ho! He dan - ces and sings to the
light heart - ed fair - y, heigh ho! His nec - tar he sips from the
light heart - ed fair - y, heigh ho! The night is his noon and his
Sharp-five
cres - - cen - - do
sound of his wings, With a hey and a heigh and a
prim - ros - es' lips, With a hey and a heigh and a
sun is the moon, With a hey and a heigh and a
Sharp-four
dim - in - u - en - do
ho! With a hey and a heigh and a ho!
ho! With a hey and a heigh and a ho!
ho! With a hey and a heigh and a ho!

SILENT NIGHT

Fr. Gruber

17
Andante
pp
1. Si - lent Night, peace-ful Night, All is calm,
2. Si - lent Night, peace-ful Night, All is calm,
pp
1. Si - lent Night, peace - ful Night, The earth is
2. Si - lent Night, peace - ful Night, The earth is
all is bright. O - ver mead - ow, hill, and dale,
all is bright. Qui - et lakes be - neath the sky
calm and bright. O - ver mead - ow, hill, and dale,
calm and bright, Qui - et lakes be - neath the sky,
Steals a mys - tic pur - ple veil. Wel - come, qui - et
Mir - ror stars that gleam on high. Wel - come, qui - et
sempre pp
Steals . . . . a veil. . . . . . Wel - - come, yes,
Stars . . . . on high. . . . . . Wel - - come, yes,
pp al fine
Night, ... Wel - come, qui - et Night.
Night, ... Wel - come, qui - et Night.
pp al fine
wel - come, O Night, . . Wel - come, qui - et Night.

THE VICTORY AT SARATOGA
Abbie Farwell Brown
Giacomo Meyerbeer
Allegro moderato
Marziale
Arr. from the Grand Opera "Robert le Diable"
18
1. Hark to the bu - gle call-ing us to bat - tle! Hors - es are neighing,
For - ward to hon - or, for-ward aye to glo - ry, Deeds that a bound in
2. Hark! how the bu-gle wakes the echoes proud-ly! Vic - to - ry crowns us;
Wave, tat-tered ban - ner, go-ing on be-fore us! Wave, rag-ged pen-nants,
1. 2. Drum, drum, drum, drum, drum, drum, drum, drum, drum,
sa - bers loudly rat - tle; Ban - ners are fly - ing, trum-pet calls are cry - ing,
bal-lad and in sto - ry! Lib - er - ty calls us, so what-e'er be-falls us,
blow, ye trum-pets, loud-ly! Hag - gard and bleeding, but the wounds unheeding,
flut-t'ring feebly o'er us! Cheer - i - ly sing-ing, wel-come tid - ings bring-ing,
drum drum, drum, drum, drum, drum, drum, drum, drum, drum,
1
Beat, lit - tle Drum - mer, lead us to the fight! Oh!
Beat, lit - tle Drum - mer, lead us from the fight! Oh!
Drum, drum, drum, drum, drum, drum, drum.
2
Fare - well, our dear ones, Fare you well to - night.
Home to our dear ones, March - ing home to - night.

EVENING SONG
Abbie Farwell Brown
Mozart
Arr. from the Comic Opera
"The Marriage of Figaro"
Andante con moto
19
1. See how the ev - 'ning floats gen - tly down, Spread - ing her
2. Come, gen-tle ev - 'ning, waft us thy rest, Hearts that are
1. The ev-'ning, the ev-'ning floats gen - tly down, floats gently, See how she
2. Come gen-tly, come gen-tly, waft us thy rest, come gen-tly, O ev - 'ning,
man - tle o - ver the town,
wea - ry, soothe on thy breast,
spreads her man - tle o - ver the town, the town. Dark
hearts so wea - ry soothe on thy breast, thy breast. O
Shades are trail - ing, mead - ows veil - ing, Fring - ing her gown.
Hith - er steal - ing, bring thy heal - ing Out of the West.
IN THE MOUNTAINS
Tyrolean
Thomas Koschat. Adapted
Con grazia
20
1. The sky is bright with daz - zling light, Tra
2. Be - fore me lie the up - lands high, Tra
Bright, is bright, daz - zling light, Tra
Lie, they lie, high, so high, Tra

mp
la la la la la la la la la. The moun-tain peak . . I
la la la la la la la la la. A brac - ing air . . will
mp
moun-tain peak
brac - ing air
fain would seek, ... Tra la la la la la la
greet me there, ... Tra la la la la la la
fain would seek,
greet me there
FINE mf
la. A - bove the clouds, a mist - y sea, The
la. A - bove the vale, ar - rayed in green, I
Now wid - er, wid - - er grows the view And
A - far, I see the snow-peaks shine, The
mf
A - bove . . . the clouds, a mist - - y sea, The
A - bove . . . the vale, ar - rayed . . in green, I
Now wid - - er, wid - er grows . . . the view And
A - far, . . . I see the snow - peaks shine, The
1
2
D.C.
haz - y moun - tain beck-ons me; climb to view the love-ly scene.
ev - 'ry sense ex - ults a - new; world is good and life di - vine.
Sharp-one
Sharp-four

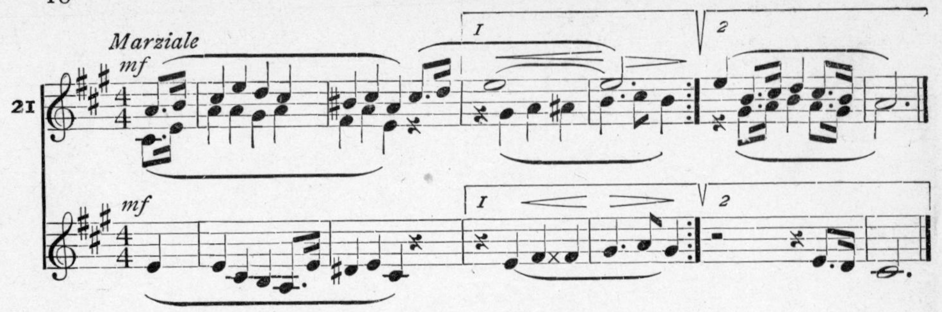
Marziale
mf
21
mf

A LIFE LESSON

THACKERAY

SCHUMANN
Arr. from the Pianoforte Composition "Nachtstück"

Andante espressivo

22

mf

1. Come wealth or want, come good or ill, Let
2. Who miss - es, or who wins the prize? Go,

young and old ac - cept their part, And bow be - fore God's
lose or con - quer as you can; But if you fail, or

might - y will, And bear it with an hon - est heart.
if you rise, Be each, pray God, a no - ble man.

Moderato
mp
1
2
23
mp
1
2

THE SUMMER NIGHT

ELIZABETH LINCOLN GOULD — J. F. NESMÜLLER

Andantino

24

1. The stars look down on field and town, While
2. The glow-worm tries to light the skies; The

1. The stars look down on field and
2. The glow-worm tries to light the

night broods o'er the sleep-ing land. A wan-d'ring breeze now
pale moth flut-ters to and fro; A-mong the trees the

town, Night broods o'er the land. A wan-d'ring
skies, Moths fly to and fro; The drow-sy

stirs the trees, Then sinks to rest at night's command. The
drow-sy breeze Lies wait-ing for the night to go. At

breeze now stirs the trees, At night's com-mand.
breeze waits in the trees For night to go.

Sharp-four
wa - ter gent - ly laps the shore; From far and near, so
last the dark - ness leaves the hill, And then is heard some
The wa - ter gent - ly laps the shore; From far and near
At last the dark-ness leaves the hill, And then is heard
soft and clear, The church bells tell the hour once more; No
lit - tle bird; He greets the dawn with soft - est trill; The
so soft and clear, Church bells tell the hour once more; No
some lit - tle bird; Greet - ing dawn with soft - est trill; The
pp
sound is heard from beast or bird; All things that wake with
stars grow gray and fade a-way; Now comes the ros - y
sound is heard from beast or bird; All things that wake with
stars grow gray and fade a - way; Now comes the ros - y
poco rall.
morn - ing light Are hushed through-out the qui - et night.
east - ern light That ends the peace - ful sum - mer night.
morn - ing light Are hushed at qui - et night.
east - ern light That ends the sum - mer night.

SUNSET
M. L. Baum
Schubert
Andante espressivo
25
1. Come, we will wander, you and I, Yonder where hill-tops meet the sky There will we sit and see de-part-ing day, . . Watch-ing it slow-ly west-ward wend its way, . .
2. Blue tint will turn to pink and gold, Pet-als of rose will wide un-fold; — All through the west the sky one ra-diant flow'r Born but to crown the qui-et sun-set hour, . .
3. Slow-ly the shad-ows then will fall, Steal-ing a-long the moun-tain wall; Home we shall wan-der stroll-ing hand in hand, . Dream-ing bright dreams a-bout the sun-set land, .
1 & 2
West-ward wend its way.
Qui-et sun-set hour.
3
Sun-set, ro-sy land. . . . . . .
(Sun-set, sun-set, ro-sy land.)

M. B. Willis
Elemér Szentirmay
Allegretto
26
1. When the night is fall - ing Plain-tive notes I hear, Through the dark - ness call - ing, Call - ing soft and clear.
Night is fall - ing, Plain - tive notes I hear, Through the dark - ness
2. Tell me what you're sing - ing, Sing - ing through the night, Ten - der rap - ture bring - ing, Bring - ing sweet de - light.
Tell me what you're sing - ing through the night, Ten - der rap - ture
"Whip - poor - will," they re - peat, "Whip - poor - will" low and sweet,
"Whip - poor - will," you re - peat, "Whip - poor - will" low and sweet;
1.2. Call - ing, call - ing clear, Call - ing, call - ing clear;
rit.
Fill - ing all the list - 'ning air with rich, ten - der strains.
But I can - not fath - om all that sweet song con - tains.
MY ROSE
Celia Standish
Luigi Caracciolo
Allegretto scherzando
27
1. When Tues-day
2. On Sat - ur -
1. On Mon - day morn my rose - bush bore no flow - er;
2. With Fri - day came the soft, pink pet - als peep - ing;

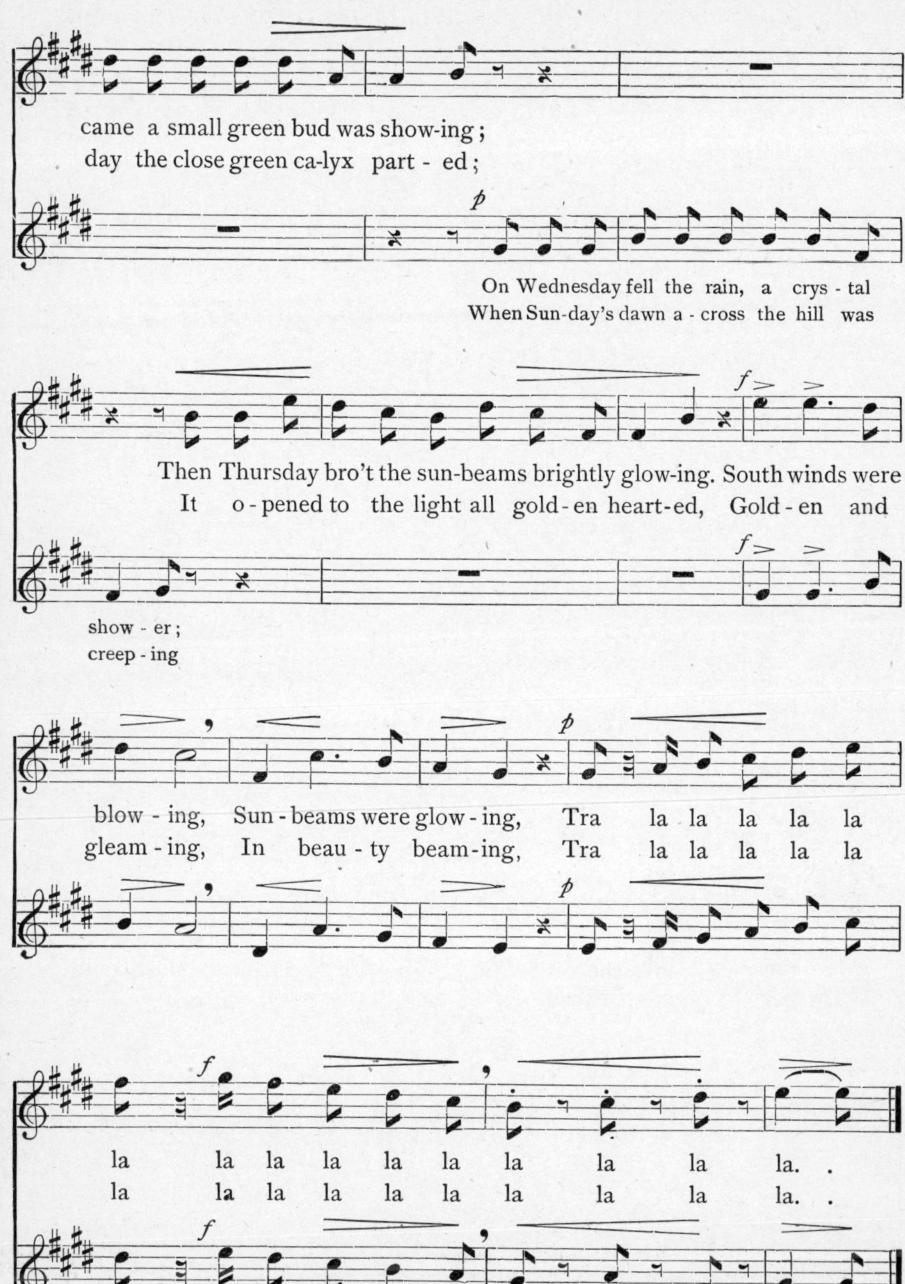
came a small green bud was show-ing;
day the close green ca-lyx part - ed;
On Wednesday fell the rain, a crys - tal
When Sun-day's dawn a - cross the hill was
show - er;
creep - ing
Then Thursday bro't the sun-beams brightly glow-ing. South winds were
It o - pened to the light all gold - en heart-ed, Gold - en and
blow - ing, Sun - beams were glow - ing, Tra la la la la la
gleam - ing, In beau - ty beam-ing, Tra la la la la la
la la la la la la la la la la. .
la la la la la la la la la la. .

THE SPINNING MAIDEN

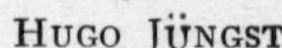
Hugo Jüngst

28

Moderato

1. Gray stands the tow - er tall, Gird - ed round by moat and wall,
2. Through sum - mer's gold - en hours, Through the springtime's sil-ver show'rs,

hm . . . . hm . . . .

There a maid - en all the day, Sings to while the hours a - way:
Through the au-tumn's scar - let glow, Through the win - ter's reign of snow,

hm . . . . hm . . . .

1. 2. "Spin, spin, the live - long day, Here with - in my tow'r I stay:

While the whir - ring spin - dle flies, To my song the wheel re-plies."

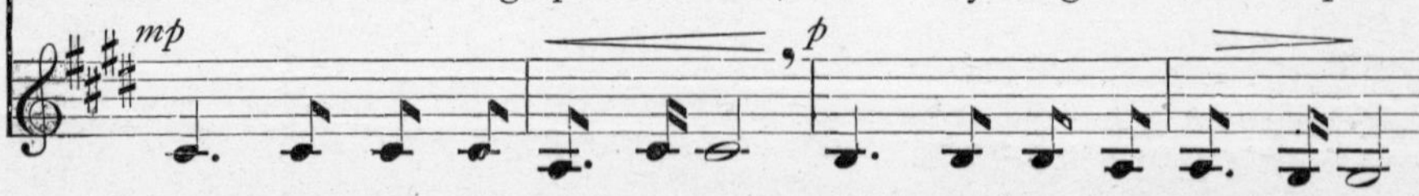

Legato
mp
mp
29
p rit. . . . .
p rit. . . . .
Grazioso
mp
p
mp
30
LAST NIGHT
HALFDAN KJERULF
Con moto moderato
p
31
1. Last night the night-in-gale woke me, Last night when all was
2. O come to me in the night-time, And close be-side me
p
1. It woke me, Last night when all was
2. O come, come, And close be-side me

still; . . . It sang in the gold - en moon - light From
stay, . . . Be-stow-ing your ten - der bless - ing To

still, was still; It sang in the gold - en moon - light From
stay, ah stay; Be-stow-ing your ten - der bless - ing To

out . . . the wood-land hill. I open'd my win-dow so gen -
guide . . me thro' the day. I long for your voice in the si -

out, from out the wood - land hill. I o-pen'd my
guide, to guide me through the day. I long for your

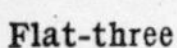
Flat-three

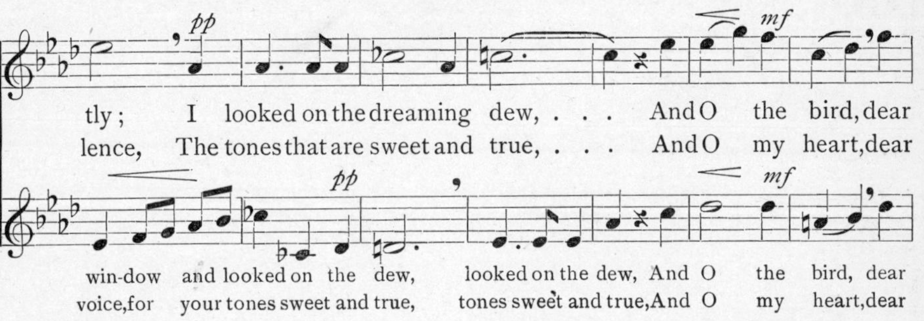
pp
mf
tly; I looked on the dreaming dew, . . . And O the bird, dear
lence, The tones that are sweet and true, . . . And O my heart, dear
pp
mf
win-dow and looked on the dew, looked on the dew, And O the bird, dear
voice, for your tones sweet and true, tones sweet and true, And O my heart, dear

rall.
p
pp
moth-er, Was sing - ing, sing-ing of you, of you. . .
moth-er, Is sigh - ing, sigh-ing for you, for you. . .
rall.
p
pp

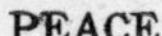
PEACE

ABBIE FARWELL BROWN

BEETHOVEN
Arr. from Symphony No. 2

Andante espressivo

p

1. Spir-it of Peace, bless thou our land; Pass o-ver all thy ten - der
earth, brood o'er the wave, Bless all this peo - ple, soothe and
2. Spir-it of Peace, thou child of love, Come from thy home in heav'n a -
land, from sea to sea, Glad-ness and plen-ty come with

32

p

hand. Brood o'er the save! Bid pas-sion be still, Let love have her
bove! Bless our dear cit - y and farm Keep war's grim a-
thee. May each fer-tile field Rich har-vest still
prai-rie and plain, Bless moun-tain and

thy ten-der hand.
in heav'n a-bove!

mp 1 2 *p*

will, Our hearts rich-ly fill, And make all strife to cease. From
larm, Pre - serve us from harm, O come be-lov - ed Peace!
yield, From woe be our shield, And bid our joys in - crease. Bless
main, Then come thou and reign, O come, be-lov - ed Peace!

Let strife cease. From
Gra - cious Peace.
Joys in - crease. Bless
Gra - cious Peace.

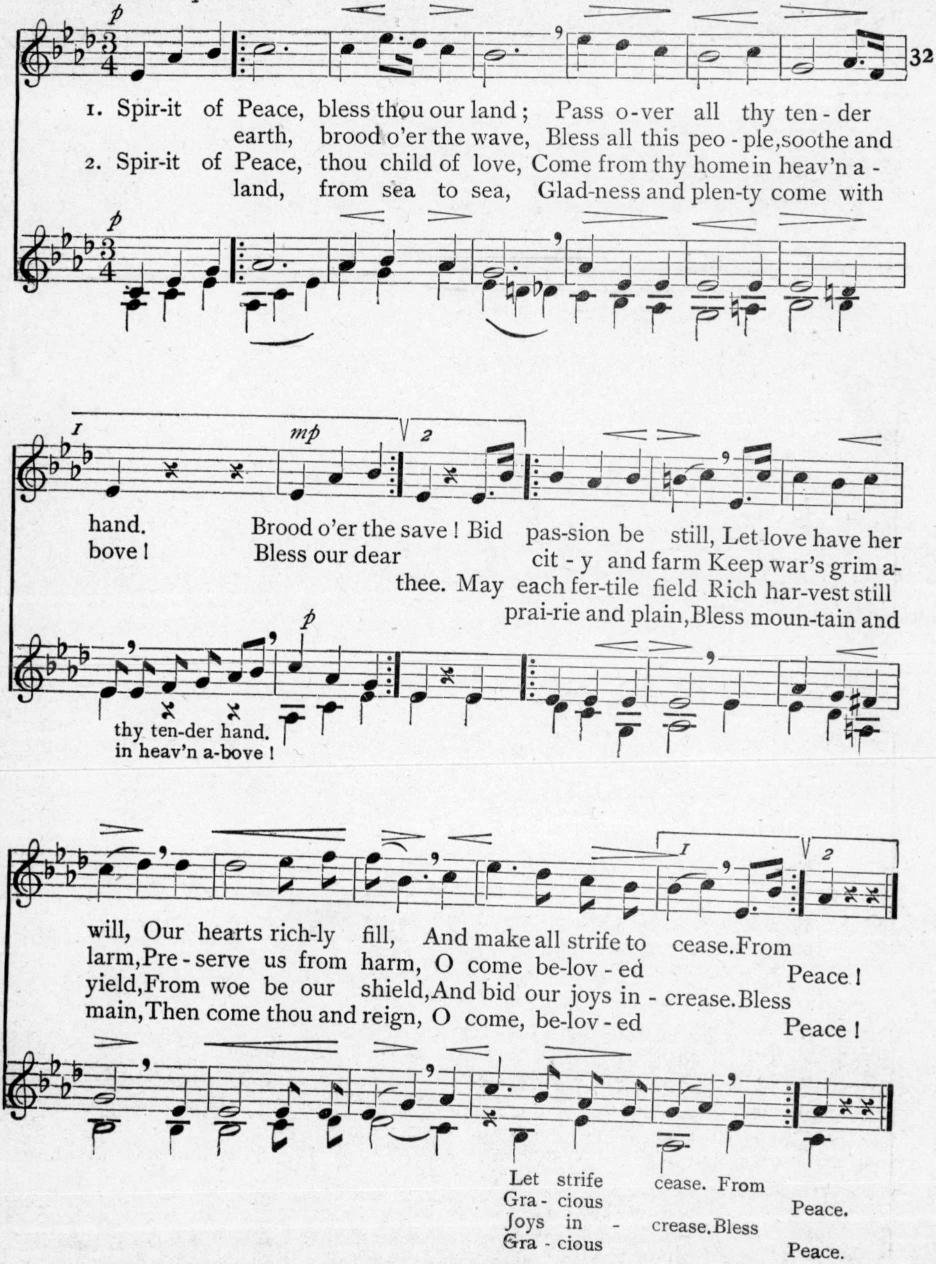

Part II

CIRCLE OF KEYS COMPLETED

Leggiero
mp
f
Key of B Major.
33
mp
f
FLING WIDE THE DOOR
Allegro con spirito
Ciro Pinsuti
34
mf
1. Fling wide the door, let in the air! The
2. Fling wide the door, let in the sun! He
3. Fling wide the soul, let in the light! The
mf
winds are sweet and flow'rs are fair And joy is all a -
has a smile for ev - 'ry one. He makes of rain-drops
whole-some thoughts that ban - ish night; The strong, pure thoughts that
broad to - day; Fling wide the door,— 'twill come this way.
gold and gems, He chan - ges tears to di - a-dems.
con - quer sin. Fling wide the door, and let them in.

Moderato
mp
mp
35
Key of
D-flat
major

SONG OF SUNSHINE

ELIZABETH LINCOLN GOULD

BENJAMIN GODARD. Arr. by HARVEY WORTHINGTON LOOMIS

Allegro moderato

p

36

1. As thro' the world a trav-'ler takes his way, If on a
2. If from his brimming cup of love and joy A draught he

p

1. As thro' the world a trav - 'ler, trav - 'ler takes his way, If
2. If from his brim - ming cup, his brimming cup of joy A

pass - er - by he smiles, ... And for an
gives some thirst-y one, ... How far may

on . . . a pass - er - by he smiles, And for an hour dull
draught . he gives some thirst - y one, How far may speed the

cres.

hour dull care be-guiles, His cheer may brighten all the day. . . . .
speed the good be - gun, With-out a touch of base al - loy, ...

cres.

care be - guiles, His cheer, his cheer may bright-en, bright-en
good be - gun, With - out, with - out a touch, a touch of

f *dim.*

Ah! who can tell? Ah! who can
Ah! who can tell? Ah! who can

f *dim.*

all the day, Ah! who, who can tell? Ah! who . .
base al - loy, Ah! who, who can tell? Ah! who . .

sostenuto *poco rall.* *p*

see? No day re - turns for you or me.
see? No day re - turns for you or me.

poco rall. *p*

. . . can see? No day, no day re - turns for you or me.
. . . can see? No day, no day re - turns for you or me.

THE MARCH OF THE MASQUERADERS

A. S. SULLIVAN
Arr. from the Comic Opera "The Mikado"

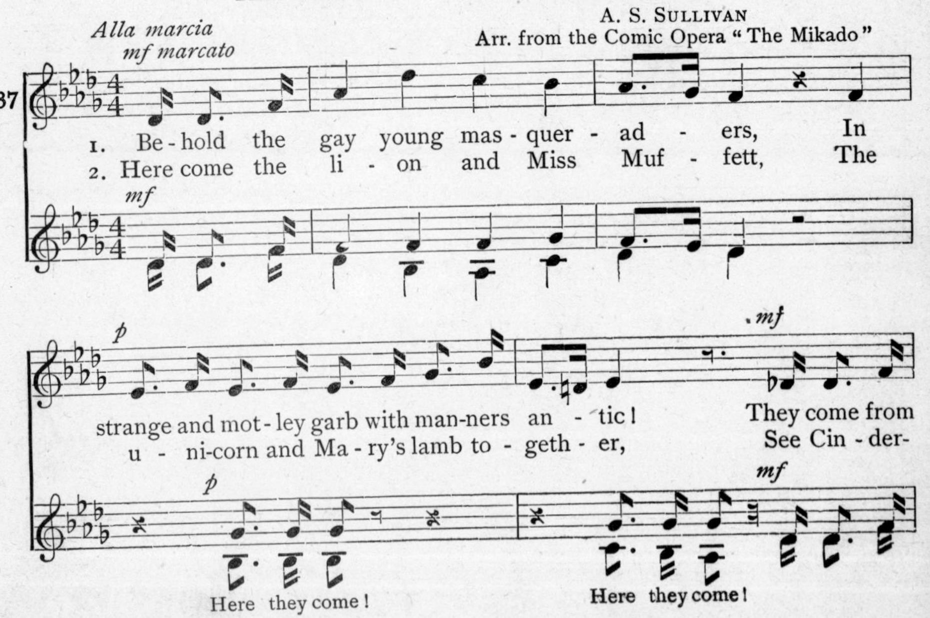
Alla marcia
mf marcato
37
1. Be-hold the gay young mas-quer - ad - ers, In
2. Here come the li - on and Miss Muf - fett, The
mf
p
mf
strange and mot-ley garb with man-ners an - tic! They come from
u - ni-corn and Ma - ry's lamb to - geth - er, See Cin - der-
p
mf
Here they come!
Here they come!

p
fair - y land and his - to-ry,—These fig-ures, some gro-tesque and some ro-
el - la with King Char-le-magne, And close behind the man all dressed in
f
p
[1] Tra la la la la la la la
f
man - tic. They come! . they come! . See the her-ald and the
leath - er. They come! . they come! . Jack and Jill and dear Red
See! they come, they
mf
la. Ah! They come, they come, they come, they come, they come! See the her-ald
Jack and Jill and
f
queen of hearts. They come! . they come! In a mer-ry throng see them
Rid-ing-hood. They come! . they come! Next to Puss in Boots, Tom the
come, ah! they come,
come, ah! they come,
and the queen of hearts come, they come, they come, they come!
dear Red Rid-ing-hood come,
3
f
march a - long, While in front goes the clown, al - ways tum-bling down.
pi - per toots. Last of all comes a bear with the wild March Hare.
f
3
3
3
3

[1] The altos only sing "Tra la."

Key of F-sharp major
38
Andantino
p
mp
f
dim - in - u - en - do
f
dim - in - u - en - do
THE FOUR SEASONS
M. B. WILLIS
HAYDN
Arr. from Symphony No. 2
39
mp Vivace
1. When the west wind is blow - ing And flow - ers are
2. When the north wind is call - ing And snow-flakes are
3. When the east wind is sigh - ing And flow - ers are
4. When the south wind ca - ress - ing The ros - es ad -
mp
1. Wind is blow - ing And flow - ers are
2. Wind is call - ing And snow-flakes are
3. Wind is sigh - ing And flow - ers are
4. Wind ca - ress - ing The ros - es ad -
mp
1. When flow - ers are
2. When snow-flakes are
3. When flow - ers are
4. When ros - es ad -
grow - ing And brooks o - ver - flow - ing, Ah! then it is spring.
fall - ing, With beau - ty en - thrall-ing, Then win - ter is king.
dy - ing And brown leaves are fly - ing, The au - tumn is here.
dress - ing His love is con - fess - ing, Then sum - mer is near.
grow - ing And brooks o - ver - flow - ing, Ah! then 'tis spring.
fall - ing, With beau - ty en - thrall-ing, Then win - ter's king.
dy - ing And brown leaves are fly - ing, The au - tumn's here.
dress - ing, His love is con - fess - ing, Then sum - mer's near.

TRIBUTE TO THE SOLDIERS

WEBER. Arr. by J. McLAUGHLIN
from the Romantic Opera "Der Freischutz"
M. L. BAUM
Adagio e con molto espressione
40 Key of G-flat major
1. Sweet - ly, with lov - ing touch, Mem - 'ry em - balms them all,
2. We have no gifts to bring, Naught can we of - fer here;
1. Sweet - ly and gent - ly, Mem - 'ry em - balms them all,
2. We bring no trib - ute, Naught can we of - fer here;
Loy - al, o - be - dient, They an-swered du - ty's call.
Grate - ful and rev - 'rent May shine a sa - cred tear;
All that man hath to give They at her man - date gave;
May we, what - e'er de - mand Time hold for us in store,
All that man can give They at her man - date gave;
May we, what - ev - er Time hold for us in store,
What trib - ute wor - thy To deck a sol - dier's grave?
Show we are wor - thy The no - ble name they bore.
rall.

Moderato
Key of C-sharp major
41
CLOSING HYMN
JAMES EDMESTON
Evening Prayer
G. C. STEBBINS
Andante
42
1. Fa - ther, breathe an ev - 'ning bless - ing, Ere re - pose our spir - its seal; Sin and want we come con - fess - ing; Thou canst save and Thou canst heal.
2. Though the night be dark and drear - y, Dark - ness can - not hide from Thee; Thou art He who, nev - er wea - ry, Watch - es where His peo - ple be.
3. Though de - struc - tion walk a - round us, Though the ar - row past us fly, An - gel guards from Thee sur - round us, We are safe if Thou art nigh.

HYMN TO OUR COUNTRY

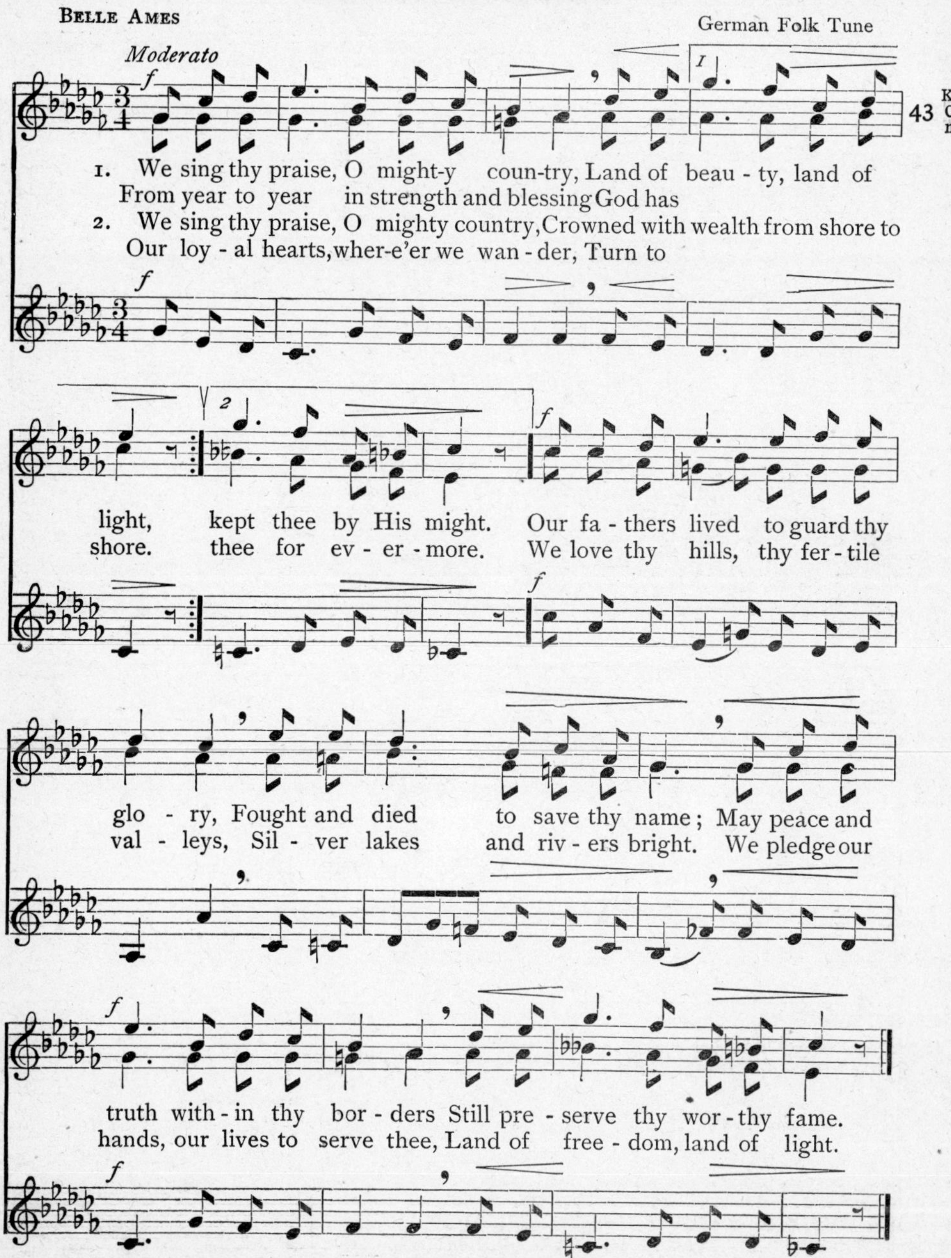
BELLE AMES
German Folk Tune
Moderato
43 Key of C-flat major
1. We sing thy praise, O might-y coun-try, Land of beau - ty, land of light,
From year to year in strength and blessing God has kept thee by His might.
2. We sing thy praise, O mighty country, Crowned with wealth from shore to shore.
Our loy - al hearts, wher-e'er we wan - der, Turn to thee for ev - er - more.
Our fa - thers lived to guard thy glo - ry, Fought and died to save thy name; May peace and truth with - in thy bor - ders Still pre - serve thy wor - thy fame.
We love thy hills, thy fer - tile val - leys, Sil - ver lakes and riv - ers bright. We pledge our hands, our lives to serve thee, Land of free - dom, land of light.

PART III

THE MINOR MODE IN CONTRAST WITH THE MAJOR MODE

Chapter I

Large Roman numerals mark major chords; small Roman numerals mark minor chords
Principal Triads
I IV V I
i iv V i
Allegro moderato
mf
Key of A minor
44
mf
Allegro moderato
mf
45
mf
mf al Fine
mf al Fine
Allegretto scherzando
p
cres.
46
cres.

f
dim.
pp
f
dim.
pp
Animato
p
p
47
RUSSIAN LULLABY
Clara Kappey. Adapted
N. Bachmetieff
Tranquillo
pp
48
1. Sleep, ah sleep, my dar - ling ba - by, Lul - la - lul - la -
2. O - ver fields and stones is rush - ing Wild the storm at
pp
1. Sleep, ah sleep, my dar - ling ba - by, Lul - la, lul - la -
2. O - ver fields and stones is rush - ing Wild the storm at
by; . . . . . . See the moon is watch - ing
night; . . . . . While the war - rior fierce is
by; lul - la - by, . . See the moon is watch - ing
night; lul - la - by, . . While the war - rior fierce is

pp
o'er thee, Watch - ing far on high. . . . . . .
near - ing With his weap - ons bright. . . . . .
pp
o'er thee, Watch - ing far on high, lul - la - by. . .
near - ing With his weap - on bright, lul - la - by. . .
pp
Thou shalt hear a won - drous sto - ry, Close thy
Forth to bat - tle went thy fa - ther, Doomed a -
pp
Thou shalt hear a won - drous sto - ry, Close thy
Forth to bat - tle went thy fa - ther, Doomed, a -
mf
wake - ful eye; . . . . . Slum - ber songs as
las, . . to die! . . . . . Sleep, ah sleep, my
mf
wake - ful eye, lul - la - by; . . Slum - ber songs as
las, . . to die! lul - la - by; . . Sleep, ah sleep, my
pp
ppp
well I'll tell thee, Lul - la, lul - la - by. . . . . .
dar - ling ba - by, Lul - la, lul - la - by. . . . . .
pp
ppp
well I'll tell thee, Lul - la, lul - la - by, lul - la - by.
dar - ling ba - by, Lul - la, lul - la - by, lul - la - by.

CHAPTER II

Principal Triads
I
IV
V
I
I
IV
V
I
Andante
mp
p
49 Key of E minor
mp
p
Allegretto
mf
50
mf
Moderato
mp
p
51
p
mp
1 f
2 f
1 f
2 f

THE SPANISH GYPSY

M. B. WILLIS — A. SALEZA

Allegretto

52

p

1. Far a-way o'er snow-capped moun-tains, Mid the sil - ver plash of
2. While I sing in rhyth-mic meas-ure, While I smile with mirth-ful

p

1. O - ver snow-capped moun - tains, Mid the plash of
2. While I sing in meas - ure, While I smile with

foun-tains, Is the home for which I'm yearn-ing, Whith-er
pleas-ure, . While the tam - bour - ine I'm play - ing, Toward my

pp *mf*

all my thoughts are turn - ing. . There the flow'rs are bloom - ing
home my thoughts are stray - ing. . Soon I'll heed my heart's fond

pp *mf*

scherzando

ev - er,— There the sum - mer leaves us nev - er. Ah! the
plead-ing, O'er the o - cean I'll be speed-ing; Then most

scherzando

sun-ny days, the sun-ny days un-end-ing, . . While the cas-ta-nets their
mer-ri-ly my jour-ney home-ward tak-ing, . . In my mem-o-ry sweet
mer-ry sound are lend-ing, . . Soft gui-tars with voi-ces
mel-o-dies a-wak-ing, . . All my sor-row here for-
blend-ing . In a tra la la la la la! tra la! . . Soft gui-
sak-ing, . I will sing tra la la la la! tra la! All my
blend-ing . . In a tra la la la! tra la! . .
sak-ing,. . I will sing tra la la! tra la! . .
tars with voi-ces blend-ing In a tra la la la la la! tra la! .
sor-row here for-sak-ing, I will sing tra la la la la! tra la! .
In a tra la la la! tra la! . .
I will sing tra la la! tra la! . .

Chapter III

Principal Triads
I
IV
V I
I
IV
V I
Con spirito
f
Key of D minor 53
f
sempre cres.
f
Andante sostenuto
p
54
ff pp
p
ff pp
Marcato con moto
mf
55
mf

THE WHISTLER

NIXON WATERMAN | G. SCHLEIFFARTH. Adapted

SOLO Allegro moderato
mf
56
1. A boy I know who's nev - er sad,
2. If all the world were like this boy,
mf DUET
1. Al - ways smil - ing,
2. Al - ways smil - ing,
And come what may he's al - ways glad.
We'd ban - ish cares that now an - noy,—
smil - ing as the morn;
smil - ing as the morn;
Al - ways smil - ing, al - ways smil - ing as the morn.
Al - ways smil - ing, al - ways smil - ing as the morn.
SOLO
Though trou - ble comes, he sings a mer - ry lay,
O nev - er let a trou - ble come to stay,
So blithe and hap - py glad - dens all the day With his "Heigh-ho!
So let us laugh our trou - bles all a - way With a "Heigh-ho!
laugh - ing as I go," He whis - tles care a - way.
laugh - ing as we go," We'll whis - tle care a - way.

CHORUS
Though trou - ble comes his mer - ry, mer - ry lay
O nev - er let a trou - ble come to stay,
So blithe and hap - py glad - dens all the day, With his "Heigh - ho!
So let us laugh our trou - ble all a - way, With a "Heigh - ho!
Smil - ing as I go," He gai - ly whis - tles care a - way.
Smil - ing as we go," We'll gai - ly whis - tle care a - way.
WHISTLE 8va
La la la etc.

Chapter IV

Principal Triads
I
IV
V
I
I
IV
V
I
Larghetto
f
p
57
Key of B minor
Vivace
f
f
58
1
2
Andante
1
2
mp
mp
mp
59

M. A. L. Lane
A. Alabieff
Andante con espressione
60
p
1. O'er the o - cean mur - m'ring low,
2. Wea - ry - winged they stay . . their flight,
p
Birds from the north - land are fly - ing to and fro,
Poise they in air, then in grace - ful curves a - light.
Birds from north - land fly - ing to and fro,
Poise in air, in grace - ful curves a - light.
cres.
They call, they cry, they cry, call and cry,
They rock, they rest, they rest, rock and rest,
cres.
Call - ing and cry - ing with voi - ces strange and high;
(They call, they cry, they cry, call and cry;)
Rock - ing and rest - ing up - on the o - cean's breast,
(They rock, they rest, they rest, rock and rest.)
p
How they dip and swing Up - on each shin - ing
Cooled by flow - ing tide, On gleam - ing waves they
p
How they dip and swing, Up - on each shin - ing
(Dip - ping, dip - ping, Up - on each wing, shin - ing)
Cooled by flow - ing tide, On gleam - ing waves they
(Rock - ing, rest - ing, Up - on the o - - cean they)

poco allegretto e molto legato
wing. O - ver the sea . . . Joy - ous and
ride. Then with a cry . . . Up - ward they
poco allegretto
wing. La la la la la la la
ride. La la la la la la la
free, Out on the tide Their wings flash far and
fly, Dart - ing a - way Be - yond the dash-ing
la la la. Out on the tide . . Their wings flash
(la la la. On the tide, the tide, Their wings flash)
la la la. Dart - ing a - way . . Be - yond the
(la la la. Dart a - way, a - way Be - yond the)
wide. No care they bor - row, They fear no
spray.
wide. la la la la la la la
spray.
sor - row. Life seems good and fair To chil-dren of the air.
la la Life seems fair to birds of the air.
(Fair to the birds of air.)

Chapter V

Principal Triads
I
IV
V
I
I
IV
V
I
Allegro moderato
Key of G minor
61
mp
mf
Allegretto
62
p
pp
pp rit.

MARCH OF THE AGES.

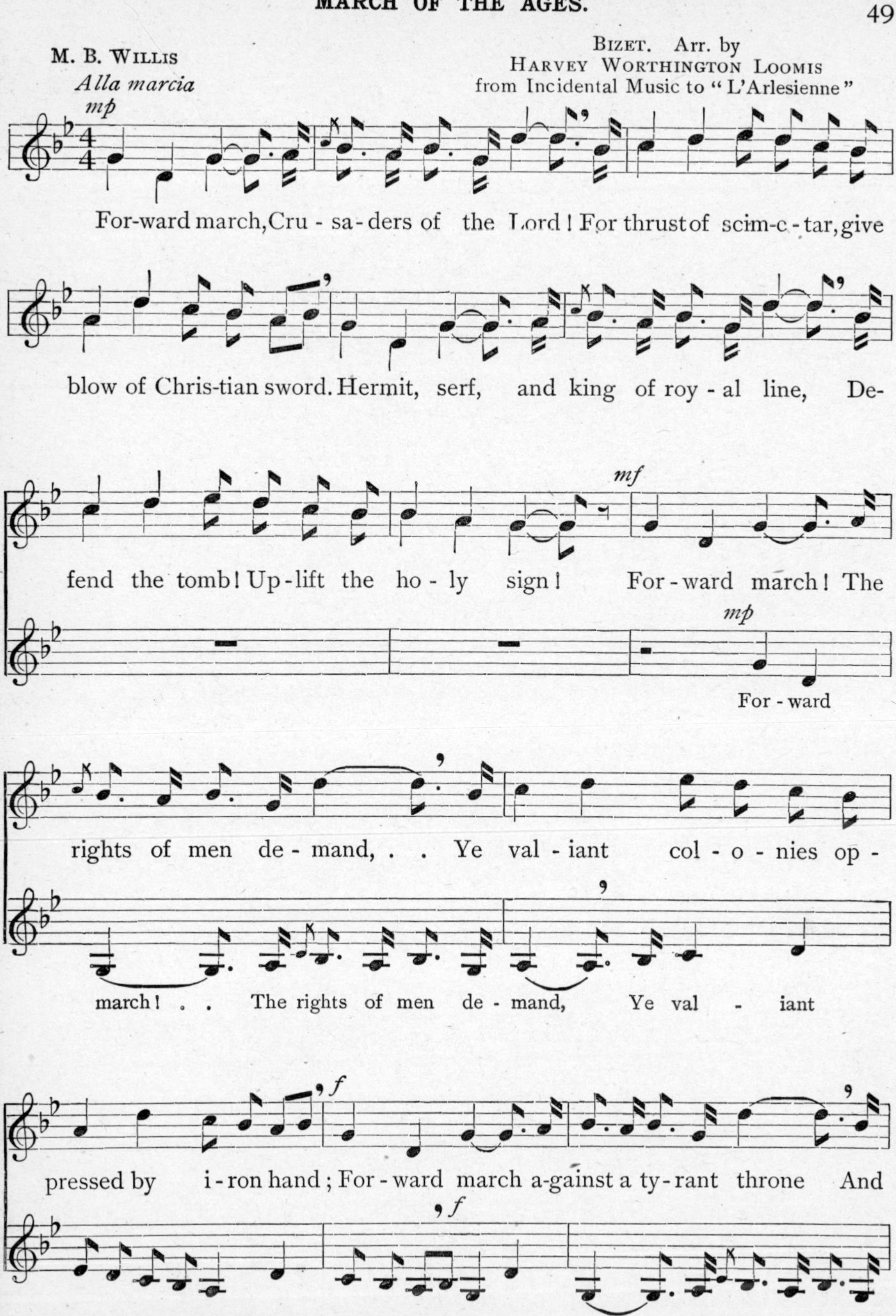
M. B. Willis
Bizet. Arr. by
Harvey Worthington Loomis
from Incidental Music to "L'Arlesienne"
Alla marcia
mp
63
For-ward march, Cru - sa - ders of the Lord! For thrust of scim-c - tar, give
blow of Chris-tian sword. Hermit, serf, and king of roy - al line, De-
fend the tomb! Up-lift the ho - ly sign! For - ward march! The
mf
mp
For - ward
rights of men de - mand, . . Ye val - iant col - o - nies op -
march! . . The rights of men de - mand, Ye val - iant
pressed by i - ron hand; For - ward march a-gainst a ty - rant throne And
f
col - o - nies op-pressed by i - ron hand; For-ward march a - gainst a ty - rant

gain the free-dom that should be your own. . .
throne . and gain the free - dom that should be your own.
poco a poco dim.
For - ward march, ye search-ers aft - er light, . Ye
p
For - ward, for - ward, for - ward,
p
kings of wis-dom who will lead us out of night; Seek the heights your
kings of wis - dom who will lead us right; . . Seek heights your
p
kings of light who will lead us right; Seek heights
pp
proph-et eyes be - hold, And prove the truth of won-ders long fore - told.
eyes be - hold, Prove the truth of won-ders long fore - told. .
pp
you be - hold, Prove the won - ders long fore - told. .

Chapter VI

Principal Triads
I IV V I I IV V I
Largo
mf
64 Key of F-sharp minor
Cantabile
p
mf
rit.
65
Adagio non tanto
mf
66

REMINISCENCE

Andante moderato HARVEY WORTHINGTON LOOMIS

67

p espressivo

Loo loo loo loo loo (loo) loo loo loo loo (loo loo)

p

mp

lo lo lo lo (lo lo) lo lo lo lo lo (lo)

mp

pp

mf

la la la la la (la) la la la la.

pp

mf

MUSIC OF AUTUMN

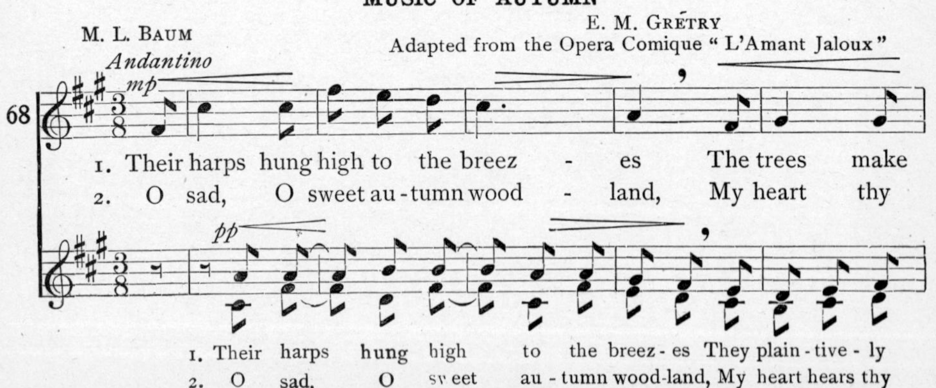
E. M. GRÉTRY
M. L. BAUM
Adapted from the Opera Comique "L'Amant Jaloux"
Andantino
68
mp
1. Their harps hung high to the breez - es The trees make
2. O sad, O sweet au - tumn wood - land, My heart thy
pp
1. Their harps hung high to the breez - es They plain - tive - ly
2. O sad, O sweet au - tumn wood-land, My heart hears thy

mel - o - dy sweet; . . Their leaves that sang once of
har - mo - ny hears; . . Re - ceives thy per - fume and
moan and sigh, they sigh; Like harps, like harps . they sigh,
voice, thy voice it hears; Thy voice, thy voice . it hears,
cres - - - - cen - -
sum - - mer, Now breath - ing rare fra - grance lie
mu - - sic, Thy mem-'ries that sol - ace, thy
cres - - - - cen - -
. . ah! they sigh, Their leaves of sum - - mer
. . O! sweet world.— Thy mem - 'ries sol - - ace
- do
f
low at their feet, And wait, ...
prom - ise that cheers, And knows . . . .
- do
p
accellerando
once that sang Now pour fra - grance sweet, fra - grance
grief and tears, My heart hears thy prom - ise and
a tempo dim - in - u - en - do
. . Sum-mer's re - turn joy - ful to greet. .
. . Joy will re - turn, ban - ish - ing tears. .
a tempo dim - in - u - en - do ritard
1. low at their feet, Sum-mer's re - turn wait-ing joy-ful to greet.
1. low at their feet, . . . wait sum - mer joy-ful to greet.
2. waits joy's re - turn Joy will re - turn a - gain, Ban-ish-ing tears.
2. waits joy's re - turn . . . Joy com - eth, Ban-ish-ing tears.

Chapter VII

Principal Triads
I IV V I I IV V I
Larghetto
Key of C minor 69
mf
Con spirito
mp
70
Alla marcia
p
cres.
f
dim.
71
THE OLD SABER
J. Offenbach
Arr. from the Comic Opera
" La Grande Duchesse de Gérolstein "
Louis C. Elson
p Moderato
72
1. 2. Drum,drum,drum,drum, Drum,drum,drum, drum, 1. 'Tis but a sa - ber,worn and
2. Those were the days of deed and
sempre p
1. 2. Drum,drum,drum,drum, Drum,drum,drum, drum, Drum, drum, drum, drum,

rust - y, Yet we re-gard it still with pride.
dar - ing When this old sa-ber still was bright,
Drum, ta ta ta ta ta ta
Drum,drum,drum,drum,Drum,drum, drum, drum, Drum, drum, drum,drum,
Long,long a-go this weap-on trust - y, Hung gleaming at a sol-dier's
When comrades brave in per-il shar - ing, March'd stern-ly onward to the
Drum, drum, drum, drum, Drum,drum, drum, drum, Drum,drum, drum, drum,
side. Foes then upon our land were dash - ing,
fight. This was our lib - er-ty's de - fend - er,
Drum, ta ta ta ta ta ta
Drum, drum, drum, drum,Drum,drum, drum, drum, Drum, drum,drum,drum,
Fier - y was Rev - o - lu-tion's dawn, Then swift-ly from its scabbard
Borne by a pa-triot tried and true. Then ev-'ry man cried "No sur-
Drum, drum, drum, drum, Drum, drum,drum,drum, Drum,drum, drum, drum,

flash - ing, In the cause of Freedom it was drawn. Ta, ta, ta, ta, ta, ta,
ren - der!" In the days when this old sword was new. Ta, ta, ta, ta, ta, ta,
Drum, drum, drum, drum, Drum, drum, drum, drum, Drum, drum, drum, drum.
Guard then the sa - ber, the sa - ber, the sa - ber, Guard then the sa - ber for
Guard then the sa - ber, the sa - ber, the sa - ber, Guard then the sa - ber for
this was freedom's brand. Guard then the sa-ber, the sa - ber, the sa - ber, For
this was freedom's brand, ta, ta, ta, ta, ta. Guard then the sa-ber, the sa - ber, the sa - ber, For
once it was drawn by loy - al hand to save our na - tive land.
it was drawn by loy - al hand to save our na - tive land.

Chapter VIII

Principal Triads
I IV V I
I IV V I
Allegretto
mp
73
Key of C-sharp minor
Allegretto scherzando
p
74

MORNING HYMN

Duke Street
Andante
J. Hatton
75
mf
1. O blest Cre-a-tor, Source of light, Thou dost the dawn from darkness bring,
2. Teach us to knock at heav'n's high door; Teach us the prize of life to win;
mf
Thou in the heav'n's most glo - rious height Dost bid the stars to-geth-er sing.
Teach us all e - vil to ab - hor, Keeping our lives all pure with-in.
THE DREAM
Abbie Farwell Brown
Gaetano Donizetti
Adapted from the Grand Opera
"Lucia di Lammermoor"
Larghetto
76
p
1. Steal-ing a - cross the slum - ber sea, Came a
2. Now when I sail the sea of sleep, Where the
p
1. Steal - ing a - cross the sea,
2. Sail - ing the sea of sleep,
Dream one night to me. Fair she was and
shad - ows dark - ly creep, Seek - ing her who
Came a dream to me. . . .
Where the shad - ows creep, . .

full of grace, Sweet was her win - some face. . . .
would not stay, Wait-ing till dawn of day. . . .
Sweet was her win - some, her win - some face.
Wait-ing, ah, wait - ing till dawn of day.
Kind were her eyes of heav'n's own blue, One friend - ly word I
Some-times I feel that she is near, Dim - ly her form I
Kind were her eyes, of heav'n's own blue, One friend - ly
Some-times I feel that she is near, Her form I
rall. pp
a tempo
mf
spoke, . . Ah, . a - way she swift - ly flew. . She
see. . . . Ah, . soft rush-ing wings I hear, . Yet
word I spoke, . Ah, a - way she swift - ly flew, swift-ly flew.
dim - ly see. . . Ah, soft rush - ing wings I hear, wings I hear.
pp
p
poco rall.
van-ished and I a-las! a-woke. Sweet Dream, farewell! Sweet Dream, farewell!
ne'er has she come again to me. Sweet Dream, farewell! Sweet Dream, farewell!

Chapter IX

Principal Triads

I
IV
V
I
I
IV
V
I
Grazioso
Key of
F minor
77
mf
f
mf
f
Comodo
78
p
p
p
p
Moderato
79
mp
mf
mp
mf

A TRUE KNIGHT

M. L. Baum
Mendelssohn
Arr. from the Italian Symphony, Op. 90
Andante
80
1. Beside the royal highway, Where blasts of winter blew amain, A ragged, moaning beggar Implored an alms in vain; . . . . . A vain, in vain;
2. He heard the beggar moaning, And drawing rein he paused in thought; He knew one hour's delaying With hazard might be fraught. . . . . He fraught, be fraught.
3. Then leaping from his charger, The weak and hungry man he fed, A-cross his saddle placed him, His mantle o'er him spread; . . . . Both o'er him spread;

cres - cen - do
p
knight then rode that way a - long, Who,
cried, "The king must call in vain, Or
cloak and rags a - side were flung, The
cres - cen - do
p
cres - - cen - - do
f
sum - moned near the king to stand, In
oth - er knights his sum - mons heed, 'Tis
knight his roy - al mas - ter knew! — "Who
cres - - cen - - do
f
dim - in - u - en - do
ea - ger pride was hast - - 'ning To
first of knight - ly du - - ties To
serves the weak, serves me best, Thou
dim - in - n - en - do
dim - in - u - en - do
pp
heed the high com - mand. . . . . . .
suc - cor those in need." . . . . . .
liege - man tried and true!" . . . . . .
dim - in - u - en - do
p

Chapter X

Principal Triads
I IV V I
I IV V I
Maestoso
mf
dim.
81
Key of G-sharp minor
mf
tranquillo
dim.
FLIGHT OF THE BIRDS
M. B. Willis
Beethoven
Arr. from the Rondo of Sonata VIII (Pathétique)
Allegro
p
cres - - cen - - - - do f
82
1. We'll fly a - way, a - way, a - way, Seek-ing in our flight e - ter - nal sum - mer time. We are
2. The au-tumn winds are bleak and cold. Sum-mer with her boun - ty could no lon - ger stay. South - ern
p
cres - - cen - - - do f
Seek in flight e - ter - nal sum - mer time.
Sum - mer's boun - - ty could no
sf
yearn - ing To be turn - ing To the
flow - ers, Sum - mer show - ers Will en -
Ah! yearn - ing, yes, turn - ing To the
Sweet flow - ers, light show - ers Will en -

land of a warm, sun - ny clime. We are
tice us to fly far a - way. South-ern
land, the land of sun - ny clime.
tice us far a - way, a - way.
clime. . . But we shall come a - gain an - oth - er
(sun - ny clime.)
way. . . But we shall come a - gain when flow'rs are
(way, a - way.)
year; Yes, we shall come a - gain when spring is here.
here; Yes, we shall come a - gain your hearts to cheer.
Principal Triads
I IV V I I IV V I
Andantino
mp
Key of B-flat minor
83
mp

James Montague
M. White
Allegretto alla burla
84
1. A boy with a rock-et Se-cure in his pock-et, — And now my sto-ry's be -
2. A spi-der mis-guid-ing A fly quite con-fiding,—And now my sto-ry's be -
3. A day warm and sun-ny, A boy wanting hon-ey, — And now my sto-ry's be -
1.2.3. Hm . . . . hm . . . .
gun,— The match-es ig-nit-ed, The crowd was ex-cit-ed, To
gun,— He crept up be-side her, This art-ful young spi-der, His
gun,— The bees came to meet him And warm-ly did greet him, Here-
. . . . . hm . . . .
see the boy near-ing the sun, the sun, And now my sto-ry is done.
web all a-round her he spun, he spun, And now my sto-ry is done.
af-ter the bees he will shun, will shun, And now my sto-ry is done.
hm . . . . hm . . . .
Principal Triads
I IV V I I IV V I
Tranquillo
85 Key of D-sharp minor

86
Andante
1. Lul-la, lul-la-by, Lul-la-by.
2. Lul-la, lul-la-by, Lul-la-by,
1. Dark the night, the wind is wailing, Lul-la-by,
Through the storm the ships are sailing, Lul-la-by.
2. Soon the sail-ors, nothing fearing, Lul-la-by,
Safe-ly thro' the darkness steering, Lul-la-by,
rall.
Men are brave, with hearts un-fail-ing, Lul-la-by,
Har-bor wa-ters will be near-ing, Lul-la-by,
rall.
Lul-la-by.
Lul-la-by,
Though the waves, crested white, Rush and roar thro' the night. Lul-la-by.
Swift and glad speeding home, Sail and spar wet with foam. Lul-la-by.
Lul-la-by,
Lul-la-by,
Principal Triads
I IV V I
I IV V I
Animato con espressione
Key of E-flat minor
87

GRADUATION SONG

M. A. L. LANE — LUDWIG SPOHR

Andantino *mp*

1. Now the sum - mer night is fall - ing, Faint-ly sounds a dis-tant 88
2. There are hap - py hours be-hind us Where our mem - 'ries long will
3. When the mor - row's sun is beam - ing, And our hopes and joys we

mp

1.2.3. Fare-well, . . fare-well, fare-well,

bell, With a ten - der ca - dence call - ing To the
dwell; May the sun - set chime re - mind us Hope will
tell, Let us min - gle with our dream - ing Lov - ing

fare-well, fare-well, fare - well, . .

rit.

day a sweet fare - well, Bid-ding day a sweet farewell.
cheer each sad fare - well, Hope will cheer each sad farewell.
thoughts of this fare - well, Lov-ing thoughts of this fare-well.

rit.

fare-well, fare-well, Bid - ding fare - well, fare-well.
Cheer-ing fare - well, fare-well.
Lov - ing fare - well, fare-well.

Principal Triads

I IV V I I IV V I

Tempo di valse

mp *mf*

89 Key of A-flat minor

mp *mf*

PART IV

DUETS, TRIOS, PART SONGS, AND CHORUSES

ROBERT OF LINCOLN

WILLIAM CULLEN BRYANT

HENRY K. HADLEY

Allegro con brio

90

mf
1. Mer - ri - ly swing - ing on brier or weed,
2. Rob - ert of Lin - coln is gai - ly dressed,
mf
1 Mer - ri - ly swing - ing on
2. Rob - ert of Lin - coln is

mp
Near to the nest of his lit - tle dame,
Wear - ing a bright black wed - ding coat;
mf
mp
brier or weed, Near to his lit - tle nest,
gai - ly dressed, Wear - ing a wed - ding coat;

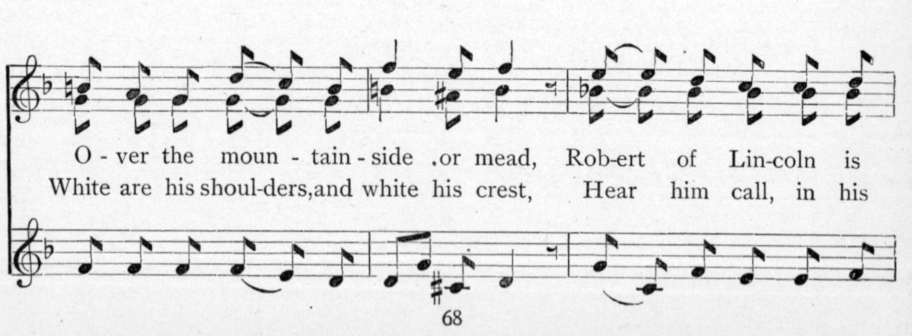
O - ver the moun - tain - side ,or mead, Rob-ert of Lin-coln is
White are his shoul-ders,and white his crest, Hear him call, in his

p
mf
f
tell - ing his name:
Bob - o - link,
bob - o - link,
bob-o-link,bob-o-link,
mer - ry note,
Bob - o - link,
bob - o - link,
bob-o-link,bob-o-link,
p
spink,spank,spink,
spink,spank,spink,
p
Snug and safe in this
Sure - ly was nev - er a
p
Snug and safe in this nest of ours,
Look what a nice new coat is mine,
p
Hid - den a - mong the sum - mer flow'rs, Chee, chee,
nest of ours a - mong the flow'rs, Chee, chee,
Sure - ly was ne'er a bird so fine! Chee, chee,
bird so fine, a bird so fine! Chee, chee,
Hid - den a - mong the sum - mer flow'rs.
Sure - ly was ne'er a bird so fine!
f
rit.
Chee, chee, Hid - den a - mong the sum - mer flow'rs.
Chee, chee, Sure - ly was nev - er a bird so fine.

MY MOTHER

ELIZABETH LINCOLN GOULD — THOMAS KOSCHAT

Moderato con espressione

91

mp
1. Dear - est moth - er mine, Oth - er love like thine, I shall
2. Dear - est moth - er mine, May I ne'er re - pine O'er a
mp
Oth - er love like thine, I shall
May I ne'er re - pine O'er a
mp
I shall
O'er a
mp
nev - - er know. Full of watch-ful care, Pure be -
hum - - ble task. All I owe to thee, More and
mp
nev - er, I shall nev - er know. Pure be -
hum - ble task, a hum-ble task. More and
mp
nev - - er, nev - er know. Full of watch-ful care, Pure be -
hum - - ble, hum - ble task. All I owe to thee, More and
yond com-pare, Nev - er fail - ing me wher - e'er I
more I see, And so slight re - turn thy love doth
yond com - pare, Nev - er fails wher - e'er I
more I see, Slight re - turn thy love doth
yond com - pare, Nev - er fails wher - e'er I
more I see, Slight re - turn thy love doth

espressivo
go. Though a - far I roam From thy sweet
ask! May my will - ing feet O - bey thy
espressivo
go. . . . Though a - far I roam From thy sweet
ask. . . . May my will - ing feet O - bey thy
espressivo
go. . . . Though a - far I roam From thy sweet
ask. . . May my will - ing feet O - bey thy
face at home, Yet it shall nev - er fade from
bid - ding sweet; But if they, heed - less, go a -
face at home, Yet it shall nev - er, nev - er fade from
bid - ding sweet; But if they, heed - less, heed - less, go a -
face at home, Yet it shall nev - - - er fade,
bid - ding sweet; But if they, heed - - - less, go,
espressivo
me. May each pass - ing year Still spare thee,
stray, Then thy ten - der eyes, So full of
espressivo
me. May each pass - ing year Still spare thee,
stray, Then thy ten - der eyes, So full of
espressivo
fade from me. May each pass - ing year Still spare thee,
go a - stray, Then thy ten - der eyes, So full of

rall.
moth - er dear! If thou wert gone, the house would emp - ty be.
sad sur-prise, Will draw me safe - ly back to thy dear way.
p
rall.
moth - er dear! If thou wert gone, the house would emp - ty be.
sad sur-prise, Will draw me safe - ly back to thy dear way.
p
rall.
CHRISTMAS
Nixon Waterman
Ciro Pinsuti
Allegro
mf
92
1. The joy - ful Yule - tide now is here, The sea - son of the
2. Though win - try winds may moan with - out, The hearth-stone grouped a -
mf
1. The joy - ful Yule - tide now is here, The glad - dest time of
2. Though win - try winds may moan with - out, The cheer - ful hearth-stone
mf
year, When all the world is full of cheer And
bout, We greet our friends with laugh and shout This
all the year, When all the world is full of cheer And
grouped a - bout, We greet our friends with laugh and shout This

cres - - - - - - - cen - -
hearts grow young a - gain; The mer - ry Christ-mas bells are
joy - ful Christ-mas day. Be - neath the mis - tle - toe and
cres - - - - - - - cen - -
hearts grow young a - gain; The mer - ry Christ-mas bells are
joy - ful Christ-mas day. Be - neath the mis - tle - toe and
cres - - - - - - - cen - -
do p cres - - - - - - -
ring - ing, ring - ing, ring - ing, And hap - py voi - ces
hol - ly, hol - ly, hol - ly, Our songs and games are
do p cres - - - - -
ring - ing, ring - ing, ring - ing, And hap - py voi - ces
hol - ly, hol - ly, hol - ly, Our songs and games are
do p cres - - - - - -
cen - - - - - - do mf
all are sing - ing, sing ing, sing-ing, "Good will, good will to
all so jol - ly, jol - ly, jol - ly, And ev - 'ry heart is
cen - - - - - - do mf
all are sing - ing, sing - ing, sing-ing, "Good will, good will to
all so jol - ly, jol - ly, jol - ly, And ev - 'ry heart is
cen - - - - - - do mf

men, Good will, good will to men, Good will, good will to
gay, And ev - 'ry heart is gay, And ev - 'ry heart is
men, Good will, good will to men, Good will, good will to
gay, And ev - 'ry heart is gay, And ev - 'ry heart is
cres - - - - cen - - - - - do
men, ... good
gay, ... is
cres - - - - cen - - - - - do
men, ... good
gay, ... is
cres - - - - cen - - - - - do
f
mf
will to men, . . . good will to men."
gay, is gay, . . . and hearts are gay.
f
mf
will, peace, . . good will to men."
gay, hearts, . . and hearts are gay.
f
mf

THE LAND OF PROMISE

Materna

Moderato
Samuel A. Ward
93
mp
1. O moth - er dear, Je - ru - sa-lem, When shall I come to thee? When
2. No murk - y cloud o'er-shad-ows thee, Nor gloom, nor darksome night; But
shall my sor - rows have an end, Thy joys when shall I see? O
ev - 'ry soul shines as the sun, For God him - self gives light. All
hap - py har - bor of the saints! O sweet and pleas - ant soil! In
through the streets, with sil - ver sound, The flood of life doth flow; Up -
thee no sor - row may be found, No grief, no care, no toil.
on whose banks on ev - 'ry side The trees of life do grow.

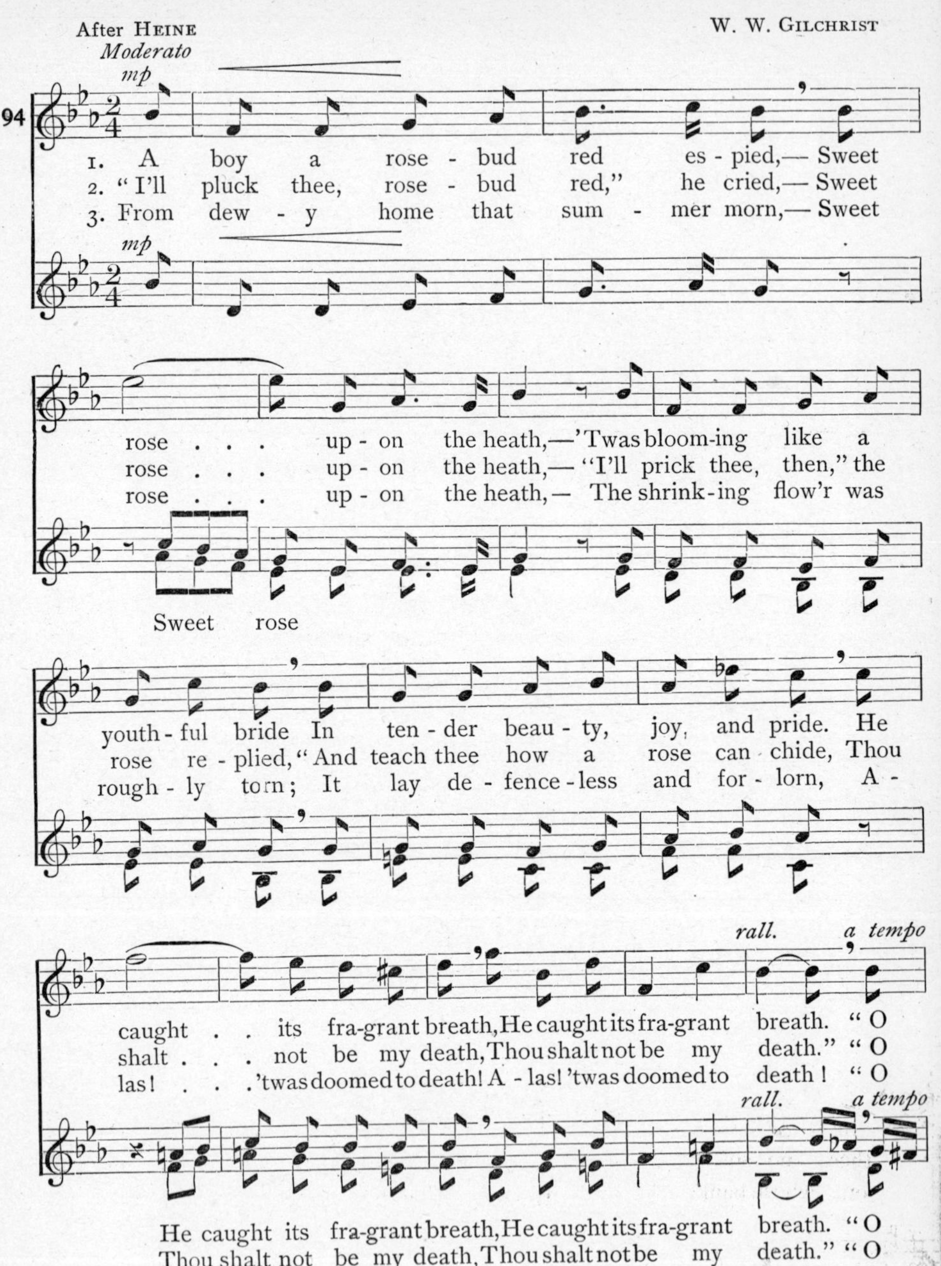
After HEINE
W. W. GILCHRIST
Moderato
mp
94
1. A boy a rose - bud red es - pied,— Sweet
2. "I'll pluck thee, rose - bud red," he cried,— Sweet
3. From dew - y home that sum - mer morn,— Sweet
mp
rose . . . up - on the heath,—'Twas bloom-ing like a
rose . . . up - on the heath,— "I'll prick thee, then," the
rose . . . up - on the heath,— The shrink-ing flow'r was
Sweet rose
youth - ful bride In ten - der beau - ty, joy, and pride. He
rose re - plied, "And teach thee how a rose can - chide, Thou
rough - ly torn; It lay de - fence - less and for - lorn, A -
rall.
a tempo
caught . . its fra-grant breath, He caught its fra-grant breath. "O
shalt . . . not be my death, Thou shalt not be my death." "O
las! . . . 'twas doomed to death! A - las! 'twas doomed to death! "O
He caught its fra-grant breath, He caught its fra-grant breath. "O
Thou shalt not be my death, Thou shalt not be my death." "O
A - las! 'twas doomed to death! A - las! 'twas doomed to death! "O

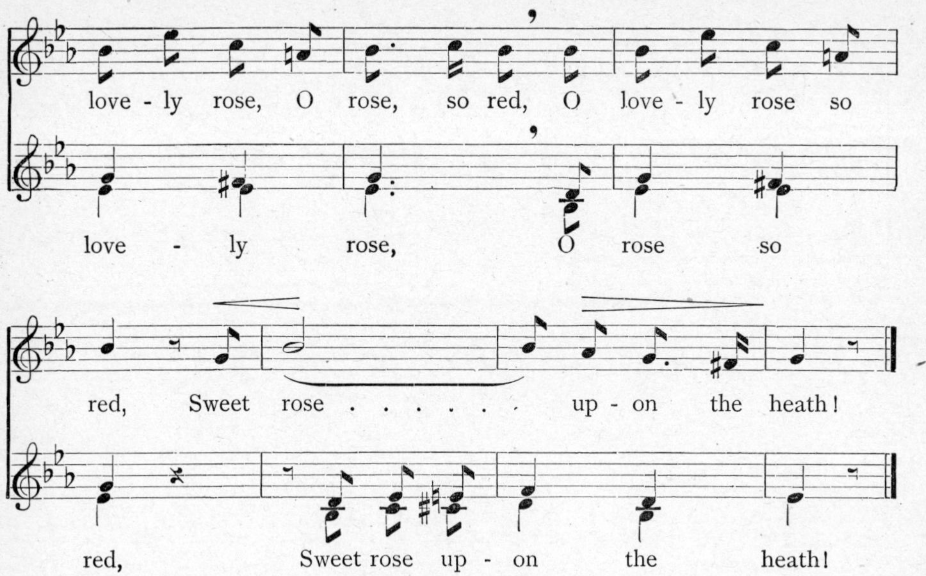
love - ly rose, O rose, so red, O love - ly rose so
love - ly rose, O rose so
red, Sweet rose . . . . up - on the heath!
red, Sweet rose up - on the heath!

SHADOW-TOWN FERRY

LILIAN DYNEVOR RICE — RALPH L. BALDWIN

Moderato

mf 95

1. Sway to and fro in the twi - light gray, This is the fer - ry to
2. Rest, lit - tle head, on my shoul-der so: One sleep-y kiss is the

mf

shad - ow town. It al - ways sails at the
on - ly fare; As drift - ing far from the

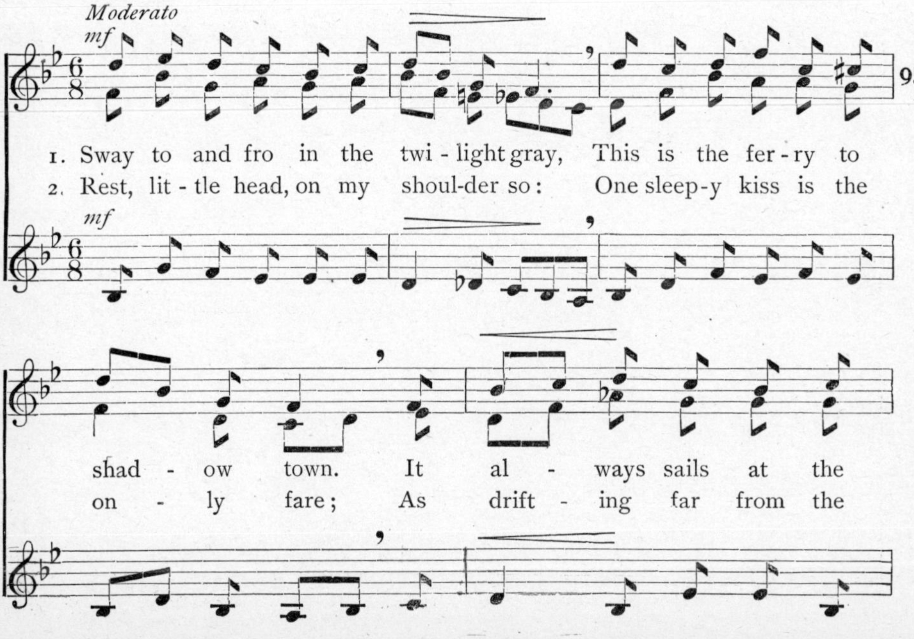

rit.
meno mosso
ppp
end of day, . . Just as the dark - ness is com - ing down.
world we go, . . Ba - by and I in the rock - ing chair.
rit.
meno mosso
ppp

I WAITED FOR THE LORD

From the Symphony-Cantata "Hymn of Praise"

MENDELSSOHN
Arr. by W. W. GILCHRIST

Andante

96 *p*

I wait - ed for the Lord, He in - clin - ed un - to

me, and heard my com - plaint, and heard my com-plaint; I

wait - ed for the Lord, He in - clin - ed un - to me and

heard my com-plaint, And heard my com-plaint. O bless'd are they that

p

hope and trust in the Lord! I wait - ed for the

p

I wait - ed for the Lord, He in -

Lord, He in-clin-ed un - to me . . . . and He heard my com-
clin - ed un - to me, He heard my com - plaint, He heard my com-
p
plaint. I wait - ed for the Lord, He in -
p
plaint. I wait - ed for the Lord, He in - clin - ed un - to
clin - ed un - to me, He heard, He heard my com-
me, He heard my com-plaint, He heard my com -
mf
p
plaint. O bless'd are they that trust in the
mf
p
plaint. O bless'd are they that hope and trust in the

Lord, are they that hope and trust, they that hope and trust in
Lord, are they that hope and trust, they that hope and trust in
I wait - ed for the Lord, He in - clin - ed un - to
Him, that hope . . . . . and trust, that hope . and
Him, are they that hope, are they that hope and trust in the
me, He heard my com - plaint, He heard my com -
trust in the Lord! I wait - ed for the Lord, I
Lord, the Lord! I wait - ed for the Lord, I wait -
plaint. I wait - ed for the Lord, He in - clin - ed un - to

wait-ed for the Lord, He heard my com-plaint, O
. . ed for the Lord, He heard my com-plaint, my com - plaint, O
me, He heard my com-plaint, He heard my com-plaint, O
bless'd are they . . that hope and trust in the Lord, O bless'd
bless'd, O bless'd are they that trust in the Lord, O bless'd, O
bless'd are they that hope . . and trust in the Lord, O bless'd, O
. . O bless'd are they that hope and trust, . . . that trust in Him.
bless'd, O bless'd are they that hope and trust, . . . trust in Him.
bless'd that hope and trust in Him.

SPRING IS COME

Wm. Allingham
J. M. McLaughlin
Leggiero
97
1. Ye coax the tim-id ver-dure A - long the hills of spring, Blue
2. The gay, trans-lu-cent morn-ing Lies glit-t'ring on the sea, . . The
1. Ye coax the ver - dure A-long the hills of spring,
2. The gay, gay morn - ing Lies glit-t'ring on the sea,
skies . . and gen-tle breez-es, And soft clouds wan - der-ing! The
noon - day sprinkles shadows A-thwart the dai - sied lea; The
Blue skies and gen-tle breez-es, And soft clouds wander-ing!
The noon-day sprinkles shad-ows A-thwart the dai-sied lea;
choir of birds on bud-ding spray, Loud larks in e - ther sing; . . . A
round sun's sink-ing scar - let rim In va - por hid-eth he; . . . The
The birds on bud - ding spray, Loud larks in e - ther sing; A
The round sun's scar-let rim In va-pour hid - eth he; The
rit.
fresh - er pulse, a wid - er day Give joy to ev - 'ry thing.
dark - ling hours are cool and dim, As ver - nal night should be.
rit.

Risoluto
HAYDN
mf
98
1. God pre-serve our Franz in glo - ry, Franz, our Emp-'ror, good and great!
2. Far and wide his sway ex - tend - ing, Blooming lands he rules a - right;
High in wis-dom, famed in sto - ry, We his prais-es cel - e - brate;
Faith and prob-i - ty un - bend-ing Form the pil - lars of his might;
mp
Love of sub-jects young and hoar-y Bind his crown of re - gal state.
For his 'scutcheon forth is send-ing Rays of jus - tice gleam-ing bright.
mp
God pre-serve our Franz in glo - ry, Franz, our Emp-'ror good and great.
God pre-serve our Franz in glo - ry, Franz, our Emp-'ror good and great.

THE DISCONTENTED PRONOUN

M. B. Willis
Henry K. Hadley
Allegretto
99
1. A pro-noun dis-con-tent-ed grew And cried in peev-ish tone, "I
2. "I thought a verb was just a verb," A-bashed, he whis-pered low. "I'll
1. A pro - noun cried in peev - ish tone, "I
2. "I'm just a verb," he whis - pered low. "I'd
hate to rep - re - sent the nouns, I want to stand a - lone. My
try an ad - verb's eas - y work. I'd like that best, I know." But
want to stand a - lone, a - lone. My
like an ad - verb best, I know." But
cas - es and my num-bers, too, Are of - ten wrong - ly used. I
when he found he had to tell Just when and how and where, He
have more work than I can do— I think I'm much a - bused." And
(I have more work than I can do— I'm much a - bused.")
grew still more and more con-fused, And answered with a stare. He
(He grew still more con - fused, and an - swered with a stare.)
rit.
I think I'm much a-bused." And
And an - swered with a stare. He

Tempo I
so, when next a verb was called, He took its place with pride, (with pride,) But
tried the man - y parts of speech, He looked the gram-mar thro', (and thro',) But
found 'twas not an eas - y task For which he had ap - plied. When
could not find a sin - gle word Whose work he'd like to do. To -
I
f slower
asked what sort of mood was his, "A hap - py mood," he said. Then
"A hap - py, hap - py mood," he said.
day if you will search in books, You'll see his well-known
f
p
ev' - ry one a - bout him laughed, Un -
Un - til he hung his head. .

cres.
til he hung his head. Then ev - 'ry one a - bout him laughed, Un-
cres.
til he hung his head. face,— A hap - py pro - noun
(well-known face,—)
(well-known face,— —)
glad to fill His own ap - point - ed place. A
(his own ap - point - ed place.)
(his own ap - point - ed place.)
hap - py pro - noun glad to fill His own ap - point - ed place.

A LESSON IN GIVING

Elizabeth Lincoln Gould
C. Chaminade
Andante sostenuto
mp cres - cen - do
100
1. Sun and breeze and fair - est flow'rs, Wide their treasure rare are fling - ing.
2. Hap-py birds their voi - ces lift, Each his sweet-est car-ol choos - ing.
3. Love - ly rose, with heart of gold, Teach, ah! teach me by thy giv - ing,
mp cres - cen - do
1. Sun and breeze and fair - est flow'rs, Wide-ly their treasure fling - ing.
2. Hap-py birds their voi - ces lift, Each, sweet - est car - ol choos-ing.
3. Love-ly rose, with heart of gold, Ah, teach me by thy giv - ing,
mp cres - cen - do
1. Sun and breeze and fair - est flow'rs, Wide their treas - ure fling - ing.
2. Hap - py birds their voi - ces lift, No sweet song re - fus - ing.
3. Love - ly rose, with heart of gold, Teach me by thy giv - ing,
We so small a share are bring - ing For these fleet - ing hours.
We a - lone, life's full - ness los - ing Hide some pre-cious gift.
Life for self is not worth liv - ing, Thy brief day hath told.
We so small a share are bring - ing For these fleet - ing hours.
We a - lone, life's full - ness los - ing, Hide some pre-cious gift.
Life for self is not worth liv - ing, Thy brief day hath told.
We so small a share are bring - ing For these fleet - ing hours.
We a - lone, life's full ness los - ing, Hide some pre-cious gift.
Life for self is not worth liv - ing, Thy brief day hath told.

DIXIE

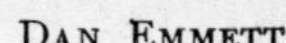
DAN EMMETT

Con spirito
mf

101

I wish I was in the land of cot - ton, Old times there are not for - got - ten, Look a - way! (Look a - way!) Look a - way! (Look a - way!) Look a - way! (Look a - way!) Dix - ie Land. In Dix - ie Land where I was born, Ear - ly on one

frost - y morn, Look a - way! (Look a - way!) Look a -
way! (Look a - way!) Look a - way! (Look a - way!) Dix - ie Land! Then I
f
f
3
3
3
wish I was in Dix - ie, Hoo - ray! (hoo - ray!) Hoo-ray! (hoo - ray!) In
3
Dix - ie land I'll take my stand, To live and die in Dix - ie, A -

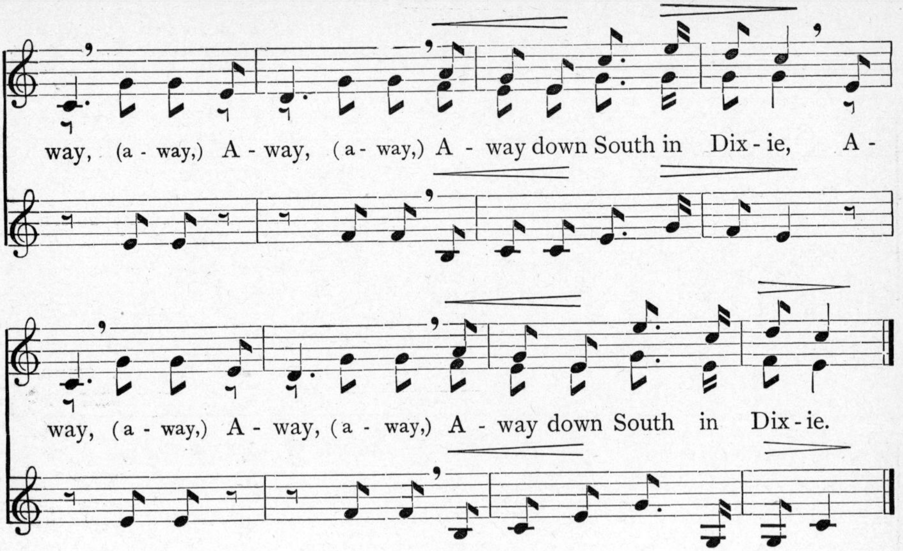

way, (a - way,) A - way, (a - way,) A - way down South in Dix - ie, A -

way, (a - way,) A - way, (a - way,) A - way down South in Dix - ie.

ALMIGHTY POWER

H. K. WHITE — Manoah — ROSSINI

102

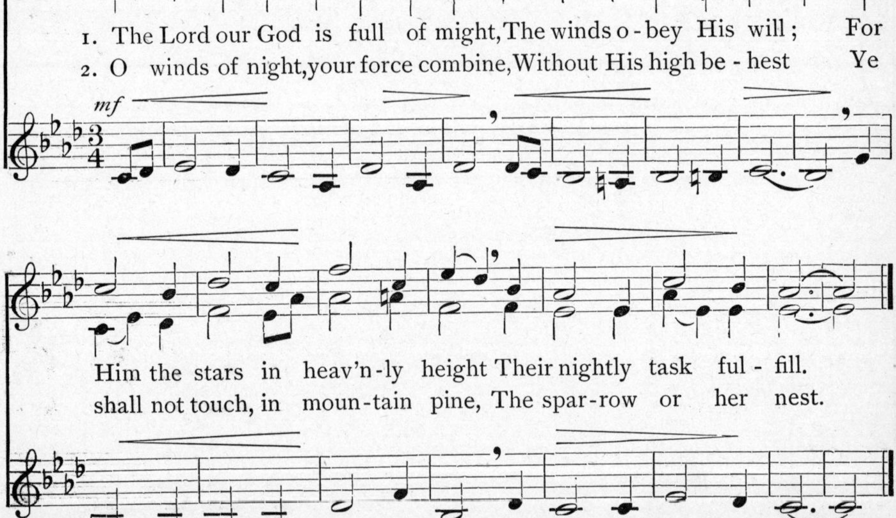
Andante
mf
1. The Lord our God is full of might, The winds o - bey His will; For
2. O winds of night, your force combine, Without His high be - hest Ye
mf
Him the stars in heav'n-ly height Their nightly task ful - fill.
shall not touch, in moun-tain pine, The spar-row or her nest.

WILL O' THE WISP

103

M. B. WILLIS

A. JUNGMANN. Arr. by HARVEY WORTHINGTON LOOMIS from the Pianoforte Composition "Will o' the Wisp"

Allegro scherzando
mp
You may think me just a sau-cy sprite And a rogu-ish lit-tle
You may think me just a sprite And a rogu-ish lit-tle
mp
You may think me just a sprite And a rogu-ish lit-tle
elf, Lead-ing men a-stray thro'-out the night, Playing pranks, then laughing to my-
elf, Lead-ing men a-stray at night, Laugh-ing to my-
elf, Leading men a-stray at night, Laugh-ing to my-
self; . . But if you'd know the truth full well, You should hear the tale I
self; . . But if you would know, . . Hear the
self, my-self; But if you would know, . . Hear me
tell. . . . If you'd know the truth,
mp
tale I tell. If you'd know the truth,
mp
well. . . . But if you'd know the truth full well, You should

p
mf
O hear me well. O - ver the marsh and the fen,
O hear the tale I tell. O - ver marsh, o - ver fen,
mf
hear the tale I tell. . . O - ver marsh, o - ver fen,
mf
Swing-ing my lan - tern high, . . . Night - ly I sig - nal to
Swing - ing my lan - tern high, my lan - tern, Sig - nal - ling,
mf
Swing - ing high, on high, my lan - tern, Sig - nal - ling,
men, Thus warn-ing them of dan - ger nigh.
sig - nal - ling, I warn them of dan - ger, dan - ger
sig - nal - ling, Thus warn-ing them of dan - ger nigh.
p
Some see . . me when the marsh I
nigh. I shine . . when . . . . the
Some, as they see me shin - ing, when I

mf
roam, Think care-less-ly my lan-tern is the
marsh I roam, some think me
roam, . . Think my shin - ing lan - tern the
p
mp cres -
light of home. Do not blame me as a sprite, Do not
light of home. Do not blame me as a sau - cy sprite, Do not
light of home. Do not blame me as a sprite, Do not
cen do
blame me as a sprite or a rogu - ish lit - tle
blame me as a sau - cy sprite, or a rogu - ish lit - tle
blame me as a sprite, or a rogu - ish lit - tle
mp
elf. The tale I tell. Now you've
elf, an elf. The tale I tell.
f
elf. Now you've heard the tale I have to tell,

heard the tale I have to tell, heard the tale I have to
tale I tell, ... tale I
tale I tell, ... Tale I
mp
tell. . . . . Heard the tale I tell,
have to tell, Heard the tale I tell,
mf
tell. . . . . Now you've heard the tale I have to tell, Now you've
cres - - - cen - - - do
Heard the tale I have to tell, to
Heard the tale I have to tell, to
cres - - - cen - - - do
heard the tale I have to tell, . . have to tell, . . have to tell, . .
mp
tell. . . So be-ware when-e'er I show my light, For I
p
tell. . . Be - ware my light,
p
. . . . . Be - ware my light,

mf
warn you dan - ger's nigh; I will swing my lan - tern
for dan - ger's nigh; I swing it
ror dan - ger's nigh; I swing it
through the night, And hold it high. Be - ware, be -
through the night, And hold it high. Be - ware, be - ware, be -
sfz
f
through the night, And hold it high. Be - ware, be -
p
sfz dim - in - u - -
ware when you see my light, Be - ware when you see my
ware, O be - ware when you see my light, O be -
ware, O be - ware, be - ware, O be -
- en - - - - - - - - - - - - - do
light, O be - ware, O be - ware, Good-night, good - night.
ware, O be - ware, Good-night, good - night.
ware. So good-night, good - night.

LIFT THINE EYES

From the Oratorio "Elijah"

MENDELSSOHN

104

Andante
sf
p
Lift thine eyes, O lift thine eyes to the moun - tains, whence
Lift thine eyes, O lift thine eyes to the moun - tains, whence
Lift thine eyes, O lift thine eyes to the moun - tains, whence
com - eth, whence com-eth, whence com - eth help!
com - eth, whence com-eth, whence com - eth help! Thy help com - eth,
com-eth, whence com-eth, whence com-eth help! Thy help
cres.
dim.
Thy help com - eth from the Lord, the Mak - er of
com - eth from . . the Lord, from the Lord, the Mak - er of
com - eth from . . the Lord, the Mak - - - er of

p
cres.
heav - en and earth; He hath said thy foot . . shall not be
p
cres.
heav - en and earth; He hath said thy foot shall not be
p
cres.
heav - en and earth; He hath said thy foot shall not be
pp
mov - ed. Thy keep - er will nev - er slum - - ber,
pp
mov - ed. Thy keep - er will nev - er
pp
mov - ed. Thy keep - er will nev - er
cres.
f
nev - er, will nev - er slum - ber, nev - er slum -
cres.
f
slum - - ber, nev - er, will nev - er slum - - -
f
slum - - - ber, nev - er, will nev - er slum - ber, will

rall.
dim.
p a tempo
sf
cres.
- - - - ber. Lift thine eyes, O lift thine eyes to the
rall. dim. p a tempo
sf
cres.
- - - - ber. Lift thine eyes, O lift thine eyes . to the
dim.
p
sf
cres.
nev - er slum - ber. Lift thine eyes, O lift thine eyes to the
cres.
p
moun - tains, whence com - eth, whence com - eth, whence com - eth
cres.
p
moun - tains, whence com - eth, whence com - eth, whence com - eth
cres.
p
moun - tains, whence . . com - eth, whence com - eth
sf
p
help, whence com - eth, whence com - eth, whence com-eth help!
sf
p
help, whence com - - eth, whence com - eth, whence com - eth help!
sf
p
help, whence com - - eth, whence com - eth, whence com - eth help!

SPRING

105

BELLE AMES

GOUNOD

Animato

p

La la la la la la la la la la

p

La la la la la la la la la

mf

1. Light - ly o - ver the wait - ing earth, Comes the
2. All the earth will be - gin to sing At the

la la la la la la To each mead - ow and
With the mag - ic and

mf

p

la la la la la la la la la la la

Spring with a smile of mirth; la la la la
wel - come ap - proach of Spring; la la la la

p

for - est and hill - top She brings de - - light. . . .
charm of her pres - ence The fields will wake. . . .
la la la la la la la la la la
la la la la la la la la la la la la la la

p
la la la la la la la la
p
la la la la la la la la la la
mf
la la With the sound of her sil - ver show'rs
On the wings of a fra - grant beeeze
la la la la la la la la With a
At the
mf
p
la la la la la la la la la
p
She will wak - en the sleep - ing flow'rs, la
She will come with the birds and bees,
cres - - cen - - - do dim - in - u -
thrill they will burst from their pris - on And greet the
touch of her fin - gers the brooks Will their fet - ters
la la la la la la la la la la la
la la la la la la la la la la la la la

en - do
FINE
p
light. . .
break. . .
La la la la la la
FINE
mp
la la la.
Soft - ly she kiss - es the trees as she goes,
Lakes that have slum-bered 'neath cov-er-lets white
FINE
p
la la la.
La la la la la la la la la
mf
O'er them her man - tle of ver-dure she throws, Cast-ing a spell of
Soon will a-wake and re - joice in the light; Na-ture, a - thrill with
p
la la la la la la la la la la la la
p
la la la la la la la la la la la la
rit. D.S.
joy - ous en-chant-ment In all her flight. . .
glad-ness and rap - ture, Will mu - sic make. . . .
rit. D.S.
la la la la la la la la la la la.
rit. D.S.
la la la la la la la la la la la. . . .

AMERICAN HYMN[1]

M. KELLER. Arr. by
W. W. GILCHRIST
Maestoso
106
f
1. Speed our re-pub-lic, O Fa-ther on high! Lead us in path-ways of
2. Rise up, proud ea-gle, rise up to the clouds, Spread thy broad wings o'er this
p
cres.
jus - tice and right; Rul - ers as well as the ruled, one and
fair west-ern world! Fling from thy beak our dear ban - ner of
all, Gir - dle with vir - tue—the ar - mor of might! Hail! three times
old, Show that it still is for Free-dom un-furled! Hail! three times
hail to our coun - try and flag! Rul - ers as well as the
hail to our coun - try and flag! Fling from thy beak our dear

[1] Music used by permission of OLIVER DITSON COMPANY, owners of the copyright

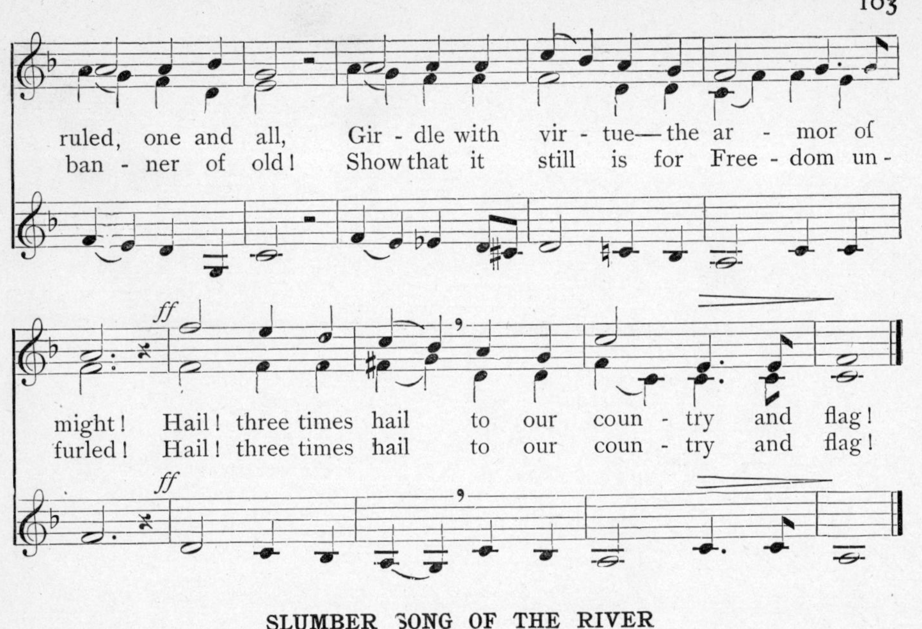
ruled, one and all, Gir - dle with vir - tue— the ar - mor of
ban - ner of old! Show that it still is for Free - dom un -
ff
might! Hail! three times hail to our coun - try and flag!
furled! Hail! three times hail to our coun - try and flag!
ff

SLUMBER SONG OF THE RIVER

M. B. WILLIS

BENJAMIN GODARD. Arr. by
HARVEY WORTHINGTON LOOMIS
from the Opera Comique "Jocelyn"

Andante cantabile

p

107

1. Slum - ber, O wea - ry men, in peace, ...
2. Far from the moun-tain tops I flow, ...

p

1. Slum - ber, O wea - ry men, in
2. Far from the moun-tain tops I

. . And I will soothe you while you're sleep - ing;
. . And go my way with peace-ful sing - ing.

peace, ... And I will soothe you while you're
flow, ... And go my way with peace-ful

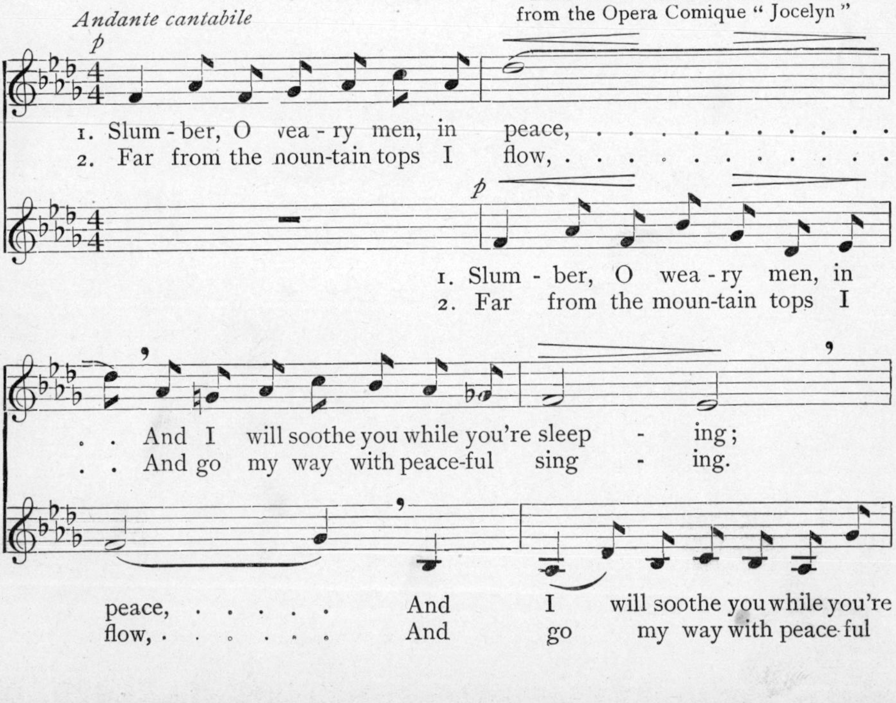

The night from toil - ing brings re - lease; . . . . . . So
My songs, wher-ev - er I may go, ... In
sleep - ing; The night from toil - ing brings re - lease, re -
sing - ing. My songs, wher - ev - er I may go, . . may
sleep, ... while stars their watch are keep - ing.
hearts . . . . . of men leave mem-'ries ring - ing.
pp
Sleep, . .
lease; So sleep while stars, while stars their watch are keep - ing. Sleep,
go, In hearts, in hearts of men leave mem'ries ring - ing.
pp
Sleep, ... the stars in heav'n are bright, ...
. sleep,
sleep,
sleep, sleep, sleep. Stars in heav'n are bright,
. . God will guard you, then sleep through the night.
pp
ppp
God will guard you, then sleep through the night.

THE RUSSIAN NATIONAL ANTHEM

Risoluto
Alexis F. Lwoff
mf
108
1. Lord God, protect the Czar! Pow'r-ful and might-y,
2. Lord God, protect the Czar! Val-iant and no-ble,
May he in glo-ry, in glo-ry reign!
Firm in his du-ty, though foes as-sail;
He is our guid-ing star, Great in peace and war, Our
Guard of our pow'r-ful land, Hon-ored near and far, The
f
faith's true pro-tect-or, Long live the . . Czar.
strength of our na-tion, Long live the . . Czar.

109
Alfred Tennyson
H. Clough-Leighter
Allegretto giojoso e leggiero
mf
1. I come from haunts of coot and hern, I make a sud-den sal - ly, And
2. I chat-ter o - ver ston - y ways, In lit - tle sharps and trebles, I
1. I make a sud - den sal - ly, And
2. In lit - tle sharps and treb-les, I
poco cres.
f
spark-le out a - mong the fern, To bick-er down a val - ley. By
bub - ble in - to eddy-ing bays, I bab-ble on the peb-bles. With
spark - le out a - mong the fern, bick - er down a val - ley.
bub - ble in - to eddy - ing bays, bab - ble on the peb - bles.
thir - ty hills I hur - ry down, Or slip be - tween the ridg-es,
many a curve my banks I fret By many a field and fal - low,
By
And
cres. un poco rit.
a tempo
twen-ty thorps, a lit - tle town, And half a hun - dred bridg-es.
a fai - ry fore-land set With wil - low - weed and mal - low.
twen-ty thorps, a lit - tle town, And half a hun - dred bridg - es.
many a fair - y fore-land set With wil - low - weed and mal - low.

MY HEART EVER FAITHFUL

Bach
Andante con moto
mp
110
My heart ev - er faith - ful, Sing prais - es, be
joy - ful, Sing prais - es, be joy - ful, Thy Fa - ther is
near; My heart ev - er faith - ful, Sing prais - es, be
My heart ev - er faith - ful, Sing prais - es, be
joy - ful, Sing prais - es, be joy - ful, Thy
joy - ful, Sing prais - es, be joy - ful, Thy

Fa - ther is near; My heart ev - er faith - ful, Sing
Fa - ther is near; My heart ev - er faith - ful, Sing
prais - es, be joy - ful, Sing prais - es, be
prais - es, be joy - ful, Sing prais - es
mf
joy - ful, Thy Fa - ther is near.
mf
joy - ful, Thy Fa - ther is near.
THE MIDSHIPMITE
F. E. Weatherly
Stephen Adams
Con spirito
111
mf
1. In fif - ty - five, on a win - ter's night, Cheer-i - ly, my lads, yo -
2. We launched the boat and we shoved her out, Cheer-i - ly, my lads, yo -
3. "I'm done for now; so good-bye!" said he, Stead-i - ly, my lads, yo -
mf
1. 2. Ho! ho! yo - ho! Cheer-i - ly, my lads, yo -
3. Ho! ho! yo - ho! Stead-i - ly, my lads, yo -

ho! We'd got the Rus - sian lines in sight, When
ho! The lands - men might have heard us shout, The
ho! "You make the boat, and don't mind me!" "We'll
ho! Ho! ho! yo - ho!
up comes a lit - tle mid - ship-mite, Cheer - i - ly, my lads, yo
brave Mid - dy cried, "Now, lads, a - bout!" Cheer - i - ly, my lads, yo
car - ry you back, or die," said we! Cheer - i - ly, my lads, yo
Ho! ho!
p
ho! "Who'll go a - shore to - night?" said he, "And spike their guns a -
ho! We reached the guns and rammed them tight, But mus - ket shots came
ho! We took him back in fear - ful plight, We pulled, each man with
ho! Yo - ho! yo - ho! yo - ho!
long with me?" "Why bless you, sir, come a - long," said we,
left and right. Down drops the poor lit - tle mid - ship-mite,
all his might, And saved the poor lit - tle mid - ship-mite,
yo - ho!

Cheer - i - ly, my lads, yo ho! . cheer - i - ly, my lads, yo
Hm, ... cheer - i - ly, my lads, yo
mf
ho! . . . . With a long, long pull, And a strong, strong
p
ho, yo ho. La la la la la la
pull, Gai - ly, boys, make her go! . . . . And we'll cheer to -
la la la la la la la la la, And we'll cheer to -
night For the mid - ship-mite, Sing-ing cheer-i - ly, lads, yo ho!
night, La la la la la, Sing-ing cheer-i - ly, lads, yo ho!

COME UNTO HIM

From the Oratorio "The Messiah"

HÄNDEL. Arr. by HARVEY WORTHINGTON LOOMIS

Moderato
112
Come un - to Him, all ye that la - bor; Come
Come un - to Him, all ye that la - bor, la - bor; Come
O come, all ye that la - bor, la - bor; Come
un - to Him, ye that are heav - y - la - den, and
un - to Him, ye that are la - - - den, and
un - to Him, ye that are la - - - den, and
He will give you rest. . . . . Come
He will give you rest. . . . . Come
He will give you rest. . . . . O

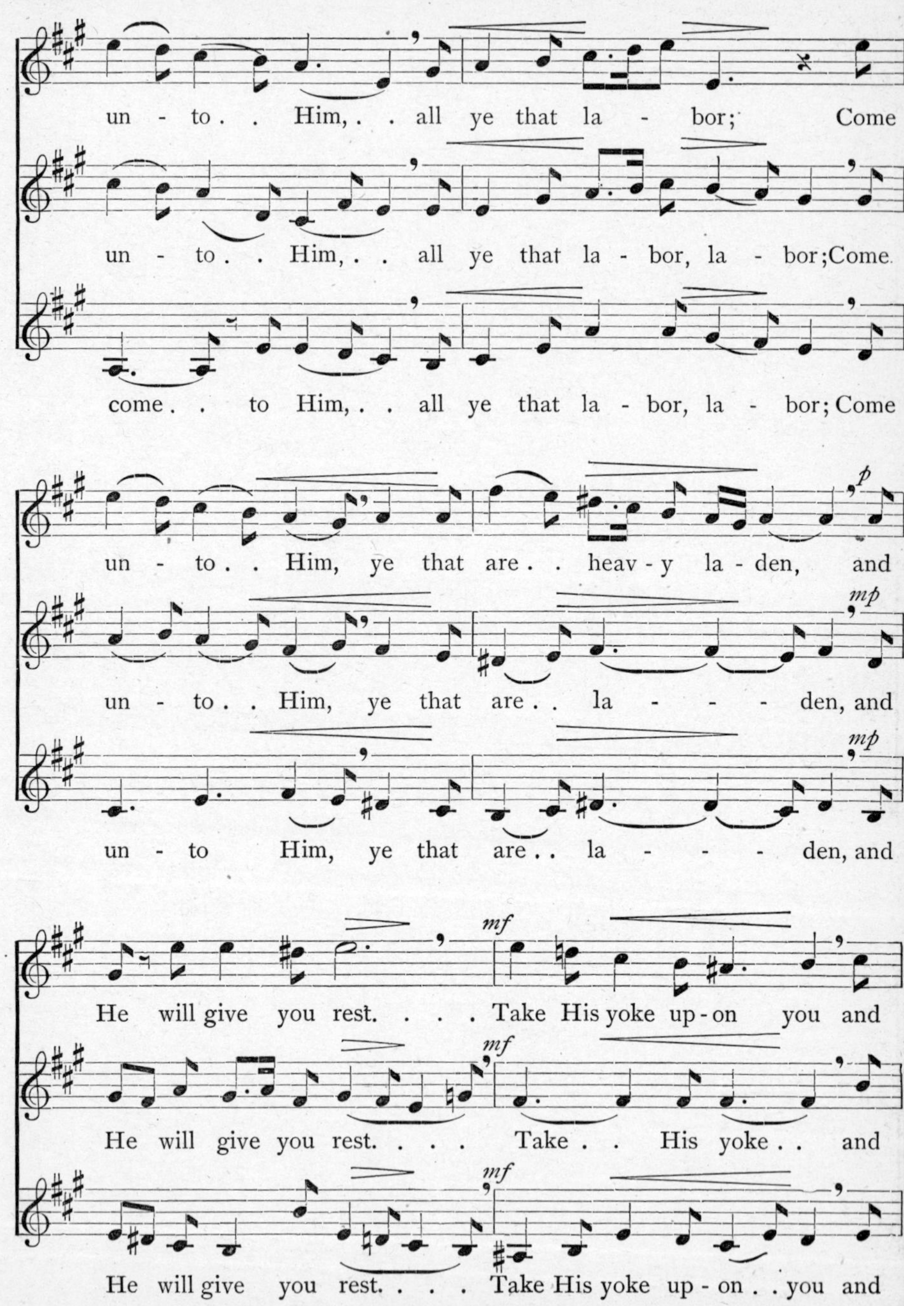
un - to . . Him, . . all ye that la - bor; Come
un - to . . Him, . . all ye that la - bor, la - bor; Come
come . . to Him, . . all ye that la - bor, la - bor; Come
p
un - to . . Him, ye that are . . heav - y la - den, and
mp
un - to . . Him, ye that are . . la - - - - den, and
mp
un - to Him, ye that are . . la - - - - den, and
mf
He will give you rest. . . . Take His yoke up - on you and
mf
He will give you rest. . . . Take . . His yoke . . and
mf
He will give you rest. . . . Take His yoke up - on . . you and

p cres - cen - - - -
learn . of Him, . . For He . is . meek . . and
p cres . cen - - - -
learn . of Him, . For He . is . meek . . and
p cres - cen - - - -
learn . of Him, . . For He . . is meek . . and
- do p
low - ly of heart . And ye shall find rest, . . And
- do p
low - ly of heart . . And ye shall find rest, . . And
- do p
low - ly of heart . And ye, ... and ye, and
ye . . shall find . . rest un - to . . your souls.
ye shall find . . rest un - to . . your souls.
ye . . shall find rest un - to . your souls.

I WONDER

M. B. Willis M. White

Allegretto giocoso
113
mp
1. 2. I won - der a - bout the words I of - ten hear, I
mp
1. 2. I won - der a - bout the words I of - ten hear; do
1. 2. I won - der much a - bout the words I of - ten hear; do
won - der; do you?
sfz p pp
you? I won - der, won - der, won - der,
you? I won - der, won - der, won - der, won - der,
mp
I won - der if a plumb - er is
O tell me if a ham - mer pre -
sempre p
won - der, won - der, won - der, won - der,
one that gath - ers plums, I won - der what a let - ter has to
fers a ham to eat, If cen - ters gath - er cents to give a -
won - der much, won - der, won - der,
won - der, won - der, won - der, won - der, won - der,

mp
let, I won - der if a sum - mer can
way; And do you think a fac - tor can
p
won - der much, won - der, won - der,
cres.
do all kinds of sums, If cas - tors ev - er try to cast a
give us facts complete, And cor - ners eat an ear of corn a
cres.
won - der, won - der, won - der, won - der,
won - der, won - der, won - der, won - der, won - der,
rit. pp a tempo
net. I won - der if a ca - per a
day? I know a - bout a pre - fix, a -
rit. pp a tempo
won - der much, I won - der, won - der,
cres.
la - dy's cape can make, If mat - ters fash - ion mats for us to
bout a suf - fix, too, I know the words that I am taught at
cres.
won - der, If mat - ters fash - ion mats for us to
won - der. I know the words that I am taught at

rit.
a tempo
mf
buy. . If I, mis - un - der - stand - ing, have
school. But though I search the gram - mar and
rit.
a tempo
p
buy, to buy. Won - der, won - der,
school, at school.
made a grave mis - take, Will some one ver - y kind - ly tell me
dic - tion - a - ry through, I can - not seem to un - der-stand the
won - der, won - der, won - der, won - der,
cres.
f
why, Will some one kind - ly tell me why?
rule, I can - not un - der - stand the rule.
cres.
f
won - der. Will some one kind - ly tell me why?
won - der. I can - not un - der - stand the rule.
ABIDE WITH ME
HENRY F. LYTE
Eventide
WILLIAM H. MONK
Allegretto
114
mp
1. A - bide with me! fast falls the e - ven - tide, The dark-ness deep-ens;
2. Swift to its close ebbs out life's lit - tle day: Earth's joys grow dim, its
3. I need Thy pres - ence ev - 'ry pass-ing hour; What but Thy grace can
mp

mp
Lord, with me a - bide! When oth - er help - ers fail, and com-forts
glo - ries pass a - way; Change and de - cay in all a-round I
foil the tempt-er's pow'r? Who like Thy - self my guide and stay can
mp
flee, Help of the help - less, O a - bide with me!
see: O Thou who chang - est not, a - bide with me!
be? Through cloud and sun - shine, O a - bide with me!
TWILIGHT AT SEA
Louis C. Elson
Rossini
Arr. from the Grand Opera "Semiramide"
Andante
mp
115
1. Stars, stars of the ev - 'ning Gleam clear on the o - cean's breast.
2. Come, time of sweet dream-ing! Swayed thus on the might - y deep,
mp
1. Gleam clear on the o - cean's breast.
2. Swayed thus on the might - y deep,
cres - cen - - do de - cres -
Day is end - ing, The world sinks to its
In its cra - dle We're rocked gen - tly to
cres - - cen - - - do de - cres -
Day is end - ing, The world sinks to
In its cra - dle We're rocked, rocked to

rest. . . . O in - fin - ite peace, Day's tri - als now
sleep. . . O mys - tic - al pow'r, Rest fills all this
rest, to rest. Peace, O peace, . . . O peace, tri - als cease. . .
sleep, to sleep. Pow'r, O pow'r. . . . O pow'r, fill this hour. . .
pp
cease, now cease. Blest hour, hour of the ev - 'ning,
(cease, Blest hour,)
hour, this hour. O, see on the ho - ri - zon
(hour. O see)
. . Blest hour,
. . O see,
All yield to thy mys - tic sway, When o - ver the
Day's slum - ber - ous eye - lids close! Night on the wide
tran - quil tide The sil - v'ry moon - beams play.
tide, the tran - quil tide, moon - beams play.
o - cean wave, Brings sooth - ing, soft re - pose.
wave, the o - cean wave, brings re - pose.
tide, the tran - quil tide, moon - beams play.
wave, the o - cean wave, brings re - pose.

TO THEE, O COUNTRY![1]

116

Anna P. Eichberg
Julius Eichberg
ppp Andante
1. To thee, O coun-try! great and free, With trust - ing hearts we
2. For thee we dai - ly work and strive, To thee we give our
ppp
1. To thee, O coun - try! great and free, With trust - ing hearts we
2. For thee we dai - ly work and strive, To thee we give our
ppp
1. To thee, O coun - try! great and free, With trust - ing hearts we
2. For thee we dai - ly work and strive, To thee we give our
cling; . . Our voi - ces, tuned by joy - ous love, Thy
love; . . For thee with fer - vor deep we pray To
cling; . . Our voi - ces, tuned by joy - ous love, Thy
love; . . For thee with fer - vor deep we pray To
cling; . . Our voi - ces, tuned by joy - ous love, Thy
love; . . For thee with fer - vor deep we pray To
cres. f dim. ppp
pow'r, thy pow'r and praises sing, . . . Thy pow'r . . and prais-es
Him, to Him who dwells a - bove, . . . Who dwells, . who dwells a -
cres. f ppp
pow'r and prais - es sing, . . Thy pow'r . . they
Him who dwells . . a - bove, . . who dwells . . a -
cres. f ppp
pow'r and prais - es sing, . . Thy pow'r . . they
Him who dwells a - bove, . . Who dwells . . a -

[1] Used by permission of Oliver Ditson Company, owners of the copyright

ff
sing. Up - on . thy migh-ty faith - ful heart, We
bove. O God, pre-serve our fa - ther - land, Let
ff
sing. Up- on . thy migh-ty faith-ful heart, We
bove. O God, pre-serve our fa - ther-land, Let
ff
sing. Up - on . thy migh-ty faith-ful
bove. O God, pre-serve our fa - ther -
p cres. f
lay, we lay our bur-dens down; Thou art the on - ly
Peace, let Peace its rul - er be, And let her hap - py
p cres. f
lay, we lay our bur - den down; Thou art the on - ly
Peace, let Peace its rul - er be, And let her hap - py
p cres. f
heart, We lay our bur-dens down; Thou art the on - ly
land, Let Peace its rul - er be, And let her hap - py
ff ppp ff
friend who feels their weight with-out a frown. Up - on thy migh-ty faith-ful
king-dom stretch from north to south-most sea. O God, preserve our fa - ther -
ff ppp ff
friend who feels their weight with-out a frown. Up - on thy migh-ty faith - ful
king-dom stretch from north to south-most sea. O God, preserve our fa - ther-
ppp ff
friend who feels their weight without a frown. Up -
king-dom stretch from north to southmost sea. O

p cres.
heart We lay, we lay our burden down; Thou
land; Let Peace, let Peace its rul-er be; And
p cres.
heart We lay, we lay our burden down; Thou
land; Let Peace, let Peaee its rul-er be; And
p cres.
on thy mighty faithful heart We lay our burden down; Thou
God preserve our fa-ther-land; Let Peace its rul - er be; And
f ff > ppp
art the on - ly friend who feels Their weight with-out a
let her hap - py king - dom stretch From north to south - most
f ff > ppp
art the on - ly friend who feels Their weight with-out a
let her hap - py king - dom stretch From north to south - most
f ff > ppp
art the on - ly friend who feels Their weight with-out a
let her hap - py king - dom stretch From north to south - most
1
2
cres. p
frown. sea, From north to south - most sea. . .
frown. sea, From north to south-most sea. . . .
frown. sea, From north to south - most sea. . . .

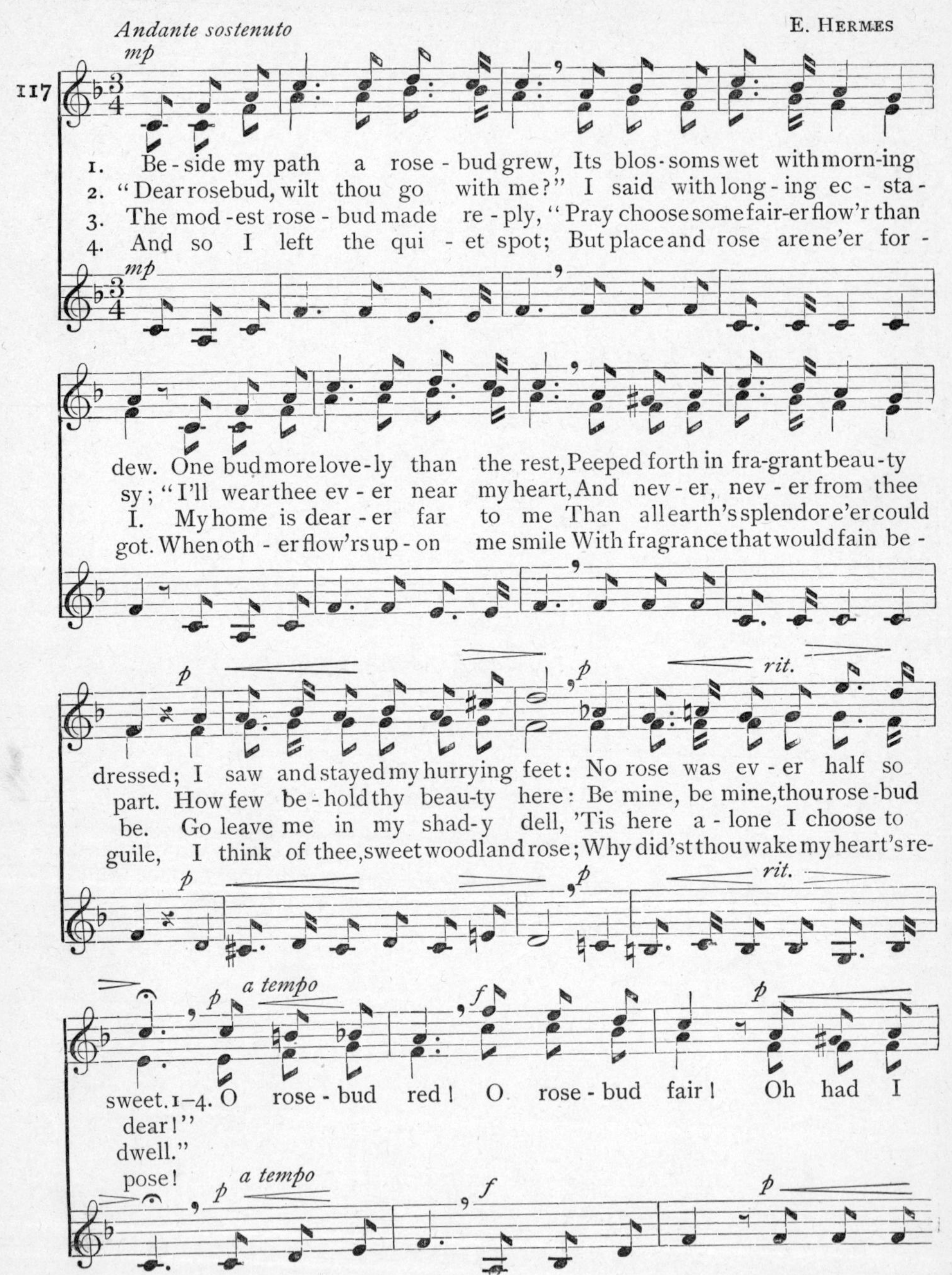
Andante sostenuto
E. HERMES
mp
117
1. Be - side my path a rose - bud grew, Its blos - soms wet with morn-ing
2. "Dear rosebud, wilt thou go with me?" I said with long - ing ec - sta -
3. The mod - est rose - bud made re - ply, "Pray choose some fair-er flow'r than
4. And so I left the qui - et spot; But place and rose are ne'er for -
mp
dew. One bud more love - ly than the rest, Peeped forth in fra-grant beau - ty
sy; "I'll wear thee ev - er near my heart, And nev - er, nev - er from thee
I. My home is dear - er far to me Than all earth's splendor e'er could
got. When oth - er flow'rs up - on me smile With fragrance that would fain be -
p
rit.
dressed; I saw and stayed my hurrying feet: No rose was ev - er half so
part. How few be - hold thy beau - ty here: Be mine, be mine, thou rose - bud
be. Go leave me in my shad - y dell, 'Tis here a - lone I choose to
guile, I think of thee, sweet woodland rose; Why did'st thou wake my heart's re -
p
rit.
a tempo
p
f
sweet. 1-4. O rose - bud red! O rose - bud fair! Oh had I
dear!"
dwell."
pose!
a tempo
p
f
p

sf
pp
nev - er seen thee there! O rose - bud red! O
sf
O rose - bud red! O rose - bud
cres.
f
pp
rose-bud fair! O had I nev - er seen thee there!
cres.
f
pp
fair! O had I never, nev - er, nev - er seen thee there!

HYMN OF THANKSGIVING

Waltham

JOHN G. WHITTIER — J. B. CALKIN

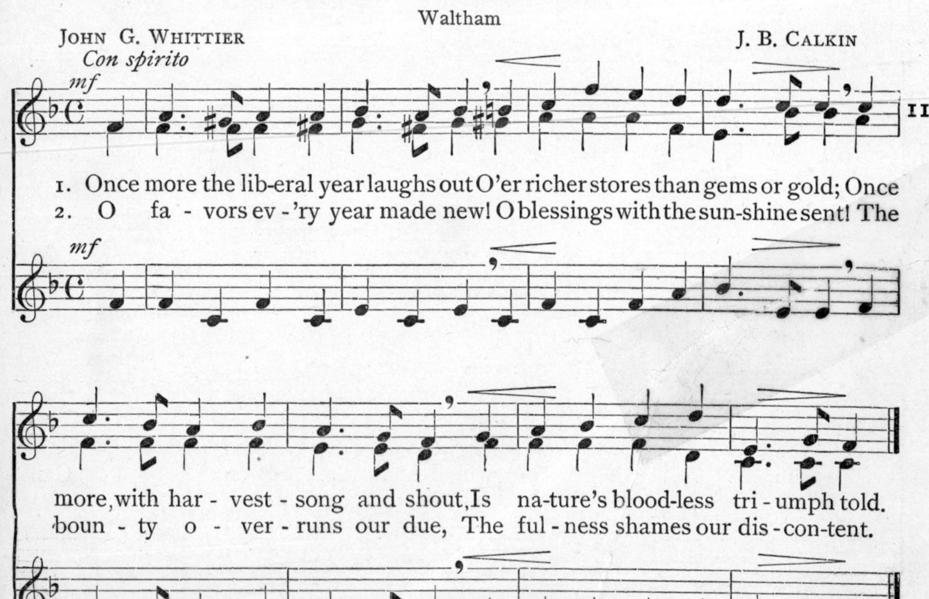
Con spirito
mf
118
1. Once more the lib-eral year laughs out O'er richer stores than gems or gold; Once
2. O fa - vors ev - 'ry year made new! O blessings with the sun-shine sent! The
mf
more, with har - vest - song and shout, Is na-ture's blood-less tri - umph told.
boun - ty o - ver - runs our due, The ful - ness shames our dis - con-tent.

THE CLOSING YEAR

M. B. Willis
Schubert
Andantino espressivo
119
1. The moments swift-ly fly, And in the changing sky The tints of
2. The sands are ebbing fast. O year that can-not last, Thy face is
Swift-ly fly, . . Changing sky, . .
Ebb-ing fast. . Can-not last, . .
ros-es die, . . For night is nigh. Fare-well, fare-well for-
o-ver-cast, . . Thy time is past. Fare-well, fare-well for-
Fare-well, fare-well,
Ros-es die. . . . . . O fare-
O-ver cast. . . . . .
ev-er, O fast-de-part-ing
ev-er, O year of cloud and
fare-well, fare-well de-part-ing
well, ... fare-well, fare-well,
year, . . . As twi-light shad-ows deep-en, Thine
sun, . . . The web which thou hast wov-en Can
year, ... O fare-well, . . .
de-parting year, Farewell, farewell, fare-well, Thine end is

p poco piu mosso cres - cen - - - -
end is draw - ing near. O days of trust and prom-ise, Of
nev - er be un-done. O days of high am - bi - tion For
fare-well, fare - well, . .
pp
pp
near, fare-well, fare-well. Days of prom-ise,
High am - bi - tion,
- - - do
p tempo primo
faith and hope ful - filled, As o'er your hours I
goals not yet at - tained, O days of toil and
Hope ful - filled, O'er your hours I
Un at - tained, Days of toil and
pp
pon - der My heart is strange - ly stilled. O
con - flict, Of joy in striv - ing gained, O
mp
pp
pon - der My heart is stilled, . . . O
con - flict, Of joy well gained, . . . O
poco piu mosso
mp cres - - - cen - - - - - - - - - do
mf
days of light and laughter, Im-bued with mag-ic spell, O
days of fault and im - pulse, Of loss and need-less fall, O
pp poco piu mosso
days of laugh-ter And mag - ic spell,
days of im - pulse, Of loss and fall,

espress. tempo primo
mp
days of storm and griev - ing, . I bid you all fare - well. .
days of stress and ac - tion, . I bid fare - well to all. . .
Days, ... I bid you all fare - well. .
p
pp
Days of griev - ing, I bid fare - well. .
Days of ac - tion, I bid fare - well. .
NIGHT
Maria Ximena Hayes
Beethoven
Adagio
p
120
1. Lo, 'tis night! and earth is hushed in si-lence, While yon-der moon leads
2. Lord of all! the o-cean tells Thy wonders, Ev - er pro-claims Thy
cres.
on her star - ry throng, Where vast un - num-bered worlds through
(through bound -
bound-less pow'r and might, We hear Thy voice a - far, a -
(a - mid . .
cres.
bound-less space are roll - ing, And o - cean waves keep time with
. . less space are roll - ing, And o - cean waves keep time with slow . .
mid the jar-ring thun-ders. Thy mys - tic voice per-vades the
. . the jar - ring thun - ders. Thy mys - tic voice per - vades the har -

rall.
p a tempo
slow and measured song. So, 'tis night! O Lord, my songs I
(. . and meas - ured song, with song.)
har - mo - nies of night. Ere I sleep, to Thee my songs I
(. . mo - nies of night, of night.)
rall.
a tempo
raise, Songs of grate - ful love and praise.

AT PARTING

Andante grazioso — HARVEY WORTHINGTON LOOMIS

p

1. Though the hour has come to part, Cour - age take, O faith - ful heart. 121
2. Naught can al - ter those who feel Bonds of friend-ship true as steel.

p

1. Now fare - well; Cour - age take, O faith - ful heart,
2. All is well, Bonds of friend - ship true as steel,

dolce. *semplice*

Space can nev - er True friends sev - er; So fare - well.
Through life's maz - es, Through time's phas - es, All is well.

dolce. *semplice*

Now fare - well, ... So fare - well.
All is well, ... All is well.

PART V

THE F CLEF

EXERCISES, PART SONGS, AND CHORUSES, ARRANGED FOR THREE UNCHANGED VOICES, OR FOR TWO UNCHANGED VOICES AND BASS VOICE.

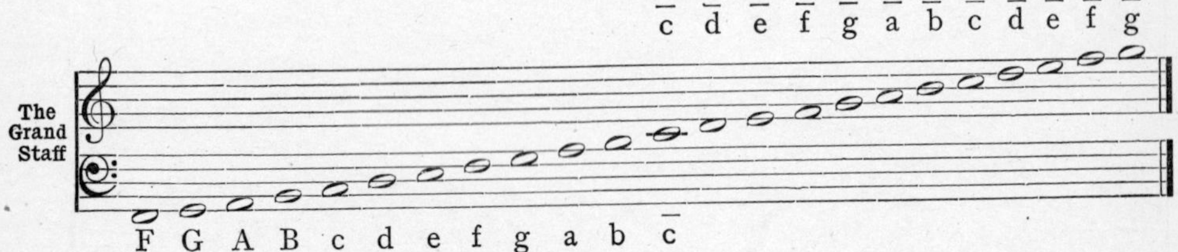
c d e f g a b c d e f g
The Grand Staff
F G A B c d e f g a b c

The Key-note and position of 1 in different keys, F clef.

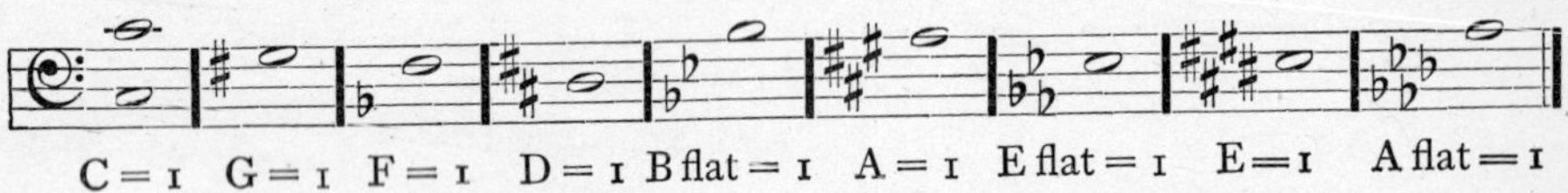
C = 1 G = 1 F = 1 D = 1 B flat = 1 A = 1 E flat = 1 E = 1 A flat = 1

Unison melodies in the F clef may be sung an octave higher by unchanged voices.

Andante
p
122

Allegro
mp
123

Allegro
mp
124

Allegretto dolce
p
125

Allegro
p
126
Allegro giocoso
HAYDN
127
Energico
mf
1
2
128
Allegro
mf
129
Allegretto
p
mp
130
Vivace
mf
131
Marcato
132
Adagio con espressione
BEETHOVEN
p
mp
133
p

Allegro giusto

134

Andante espress.

135

Allegro

136

PUCCINI
From the Grand Opera "La Bohème"

Allegretto giocoso

137

DANCING OF LONG AGO

MOZART
From the Comic Opera "The Marriage of Figaro"

Allegretto
p non legato
138

1. La-dies and gal-lants of old in dan-cing Stepped to the
2. Quaint-ly they courte-sied, their part - ners meet-ing, Back-ward and

cres.

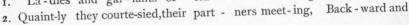

mu - sic of spin - et en - tran - cing, Grace-ful - ly bend-ing and
for - ward, ad - van - cing, re - treat - ing. Such was the dan - cing of

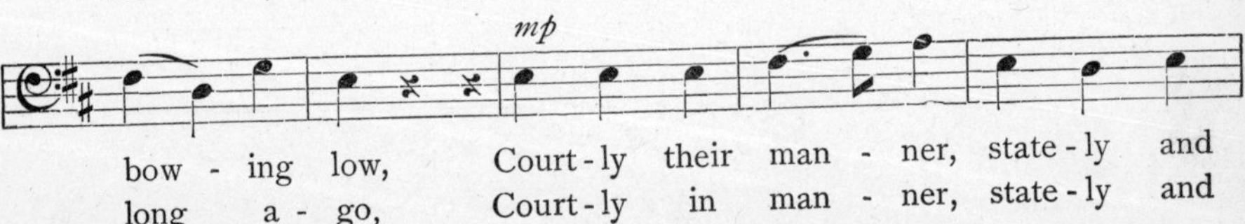
mp

bow - ing low, Court - ly their man - ner, state - ly and
long a - go, Court - ly in man - ner, state - ly and

p

slow, Court - ly their man - ner, state - ly and slow.
slow, Court - ly in man - ner, state - ly and slow.

BELIEVE ME, IF ALL THOSE ENDEARING YOUNG CHARMS

THOMAS MOORE

Irish Folk Song

Allegretto

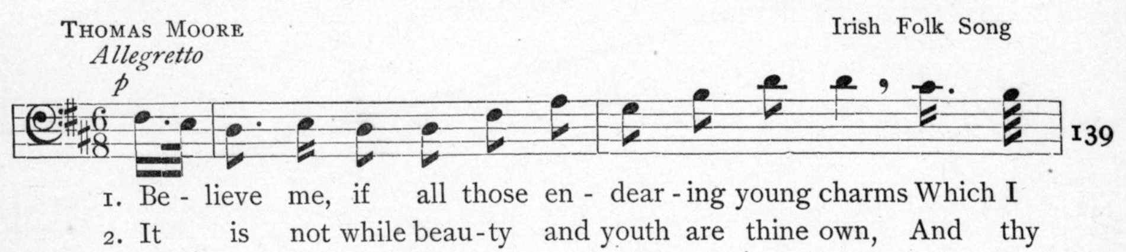
p

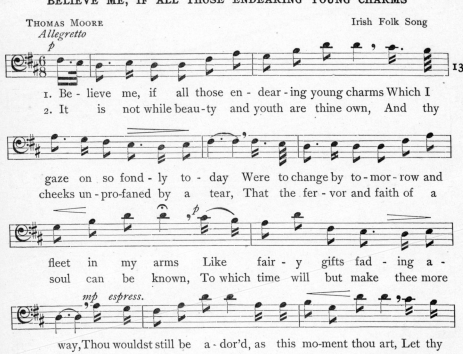

139

1. Be - lieve me, if all those en - dear - ing young charms Which I
2. It is not while beau - ty and youth are thine own, And thy

gaze on so fond - ly to - day Were to change by to - mor - row and
cheeks un - pro-faned by a tear, That the fer - vor and faith of a

p

fleet in my arms Like fair - y gifts fad - ing a -
soul can be known, To which time will but make thee more

mp espress.

way, Thou wouldst still be a - dor'd, as this mo-ment thou art, Let thy
dear; No, the heart that has tru - ly loved nev - er for - gets, But as

p

love - li - ness fade as it will, And a-round the dear ru - in each
tru - ly loves on to the close, As the sun - flow - er turns on her

wish of my heart Would en - twine it - self ver - dant - ly still.
god, when he sets, The same look which she turn'd when he rose.

Each part of Nos. 140, 141, 142 and 143 may be sung as a separate melody

Vivace
140
p
Andante
p
141
p
Allegro
mp
142
mp
Vivace
p
143
p

No. 144 is to be sung by the three upper voices, or by the two upper voices and the bass voice.

Andante
mf
mp
144
mf
p
f

Sarah F. Adams
A. S. Sullivan
Allegretto espress.
145
1. Near - er, my God, to Thee, Near - er to Thee! E'en though it
2. Though like the wan - der - er, The sun gone down, Dark - ness be
be a cross That rais - eth me, Still all my song shall be,
o - ver me, My rest a stone, Yet in my dreams I'd be
Near - er, my God, to Thee, Near - er, my God, to Thee, Near - er to Thee!
rall.

[1]To be sung by the three upper voices, or by the two upper voices and the bass.

ALLELUIA[1]

Tr. by FRANCIS POTT PALESTRINA

146

Maestoso
mf
Al - le - lu - ia! Al - le - lu - ia! Al - le - lu - ia!
f
ff
mf marcato
mp
1. The strife is o'er, the bat - tle done; The vic - to - ry of life is
2. The pow'rs of death have done their worst; The Lord their le - gions hath dis -
won; The song of tri - umph has be - gun; Al - le - lu - ia!
persed; Let shouts of ho - ly joy out-burst; Al - le - lu - ia!

[1] To be sung by the three upper voices alone, or by the two upper voices and the bass.

MISS ALGEBRA[1]

M. B. WILLIS — H. L. HEARTZ

Allegro grazioso
136
p
1. Miss Al - ge - bra thought she was grow - ing too wise To
Miss Al - ge - bra thought her - self . . too wise To
2. She talked of e - qua - tions in x and in y, Of
She talked of e - qua - tions, x . . and y, Of
3. But when she at - tempt - ed so - lu - tions to make, Her
But when she so - lu - tions tried to make, Her
4. In can - cel - ling, frac - tions, and fac - tor - ing terms, What -
In can - cel - ling, frac - tions, fac - t'ring terms, What -
p
1. Miss Al - ge - bra thought her - self too wise To
2. She talked of e qua - tions, x and y, Of
3. But when she so - lu - tions tried to make, Her
4. In can - cel - ling, frac - tions, fac - t'ring terms, What -
p
cres.
need Dame A - rith - me - tic's aid, . . . Ex - am - ples in part - ner - ship,
need, to need Dame A - rith - me - tic's aid, For part - ner - ship and
prob - lems in a, b, and c, ... Of n co - ef - fi - cients, quad -
prob - lems, prob - lems in a, b, and c, Of ma - ny co - ef -
er - ror was quick - ly re - vealed, . . With - in all the prob - lems, both
er - ror, er - ror was quick - ly re - vealed, With - in the prob - lems,
ev - er ex - am - ple was shown, . . No steps could be tak - en, no
e'er ex - am - ple, ex - am - ple was shown No sum was done, no
cres.
need, to need Dame A - rith - me - tic's aid, Part - ner - ship and
prob - lems, prob - lems in a, b, and c, Ma - ny co - ef -
er - ror, er - ror was quick - ly re - vealed, In the prob - lems,
e'er ex - am - ple, ex - am - ple was shown, Nought was done, no
cres.

* To be sung by the three upper voices alone or by the two upper voices and the bass.

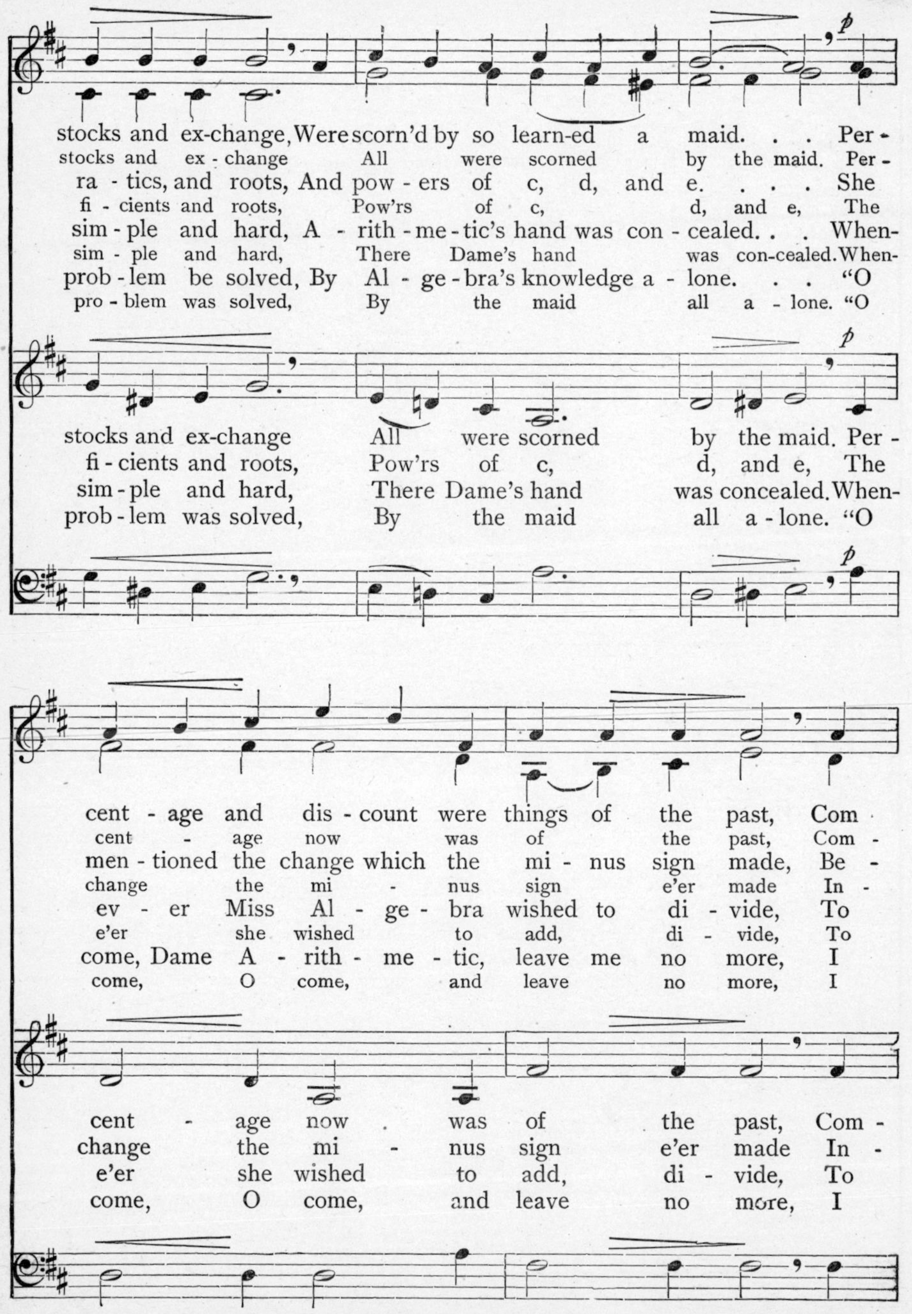

stocks and ex-change, Were scorn'd by so learn-ed a maid. . . Per -
stocks and ex - change All were scorned by the maid. Per -
ra - tics, and roots, And pow - ers of c, d, and e. . . . She
fi - cients and roots, Pow'rs of c, d, and e, The
sim - ple and hard, A - rith - me - tic's hand was con - cealed. . . When-
sim - ple and hard, There Dame's hand was con-cealed. When-
prob - lem be solved, By Al - ge - bra's knowledge a - lone. . . "O
pro - blem was solved, By the maid all a - lone. "O
stocks and ex-change All were scorned by the maid. Per -
fi - cients and roots, Pow'rs of c, d, and e, The
sim - ple and hard, There Dame's hand was concealed. When-
prob - lem was solved, By the maid all a - lone. "O
cent - age and dis - count were things of the past, Com
cent - age now was of the past, Com -
men - tioned the change which the mi - nus sign made, Be -
change the mi - nus sign e'er made In -
ev - er Miss Al - ge - bra wished to di - vide, To
e'er she wished to add, di - vide, To
come, Dame A - rith - me - tic, leave me no more, I
come, O come, and leave no more, I
cent - age now was of the past, Com -
change the mi - nus sign e'er made In -
e'er she wished to add, di - vide, To
come, O come, and leave no more, I

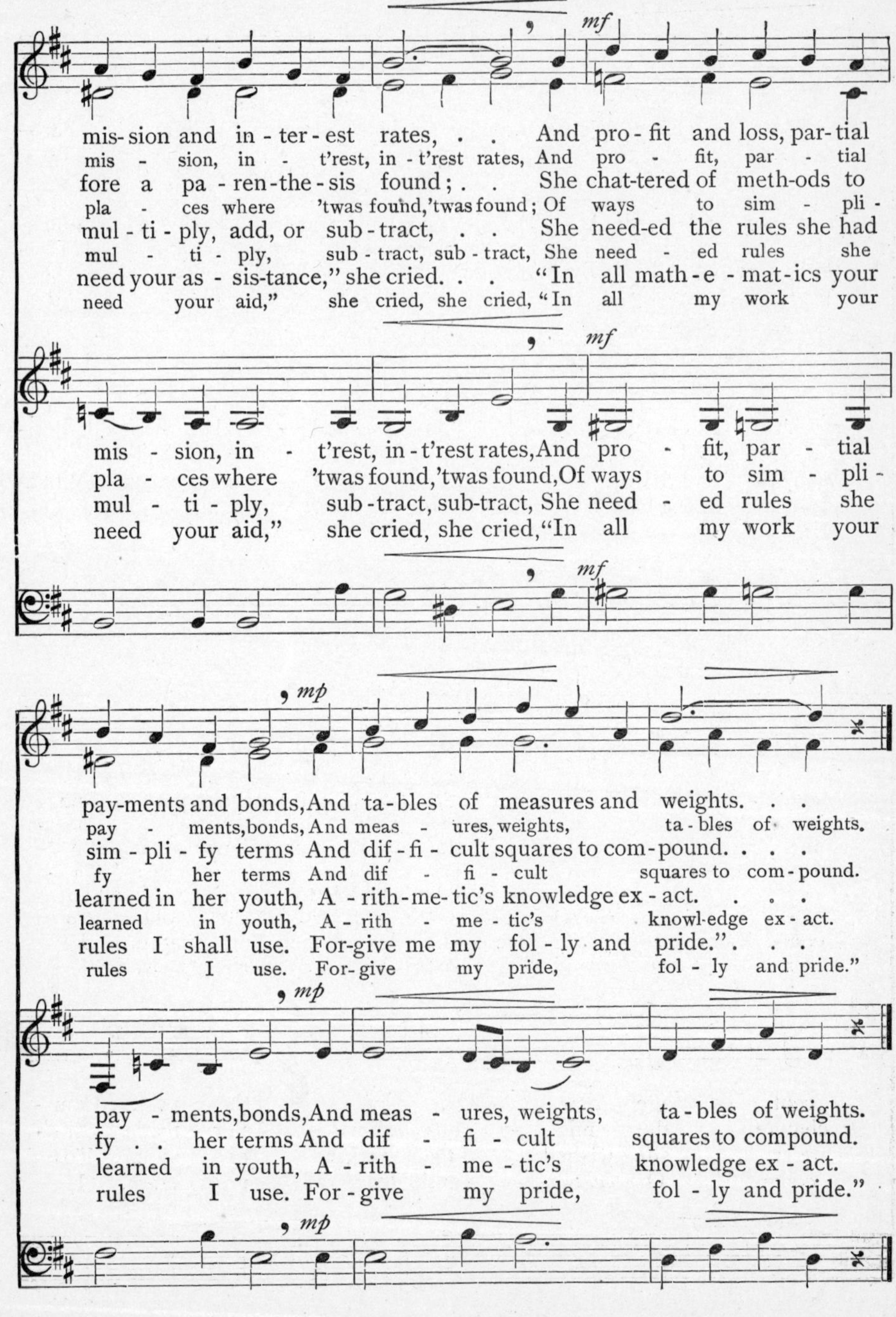
mf
mis-sion and in-ter-est rates, . . And pro-fit and loss, par-tial
mis - sion, in - t'rest, in-t'rest rates, And pro - fit, par - tial
fore a pa-ren-the-sis found; . . She chat-tered of meth-ods to
pla - ces where 'twas found,'twas found; Of ways to sim - pli -
mul-ti-ply, add, or sub-tract, . . She need-ed the rules she had
mul - ti - ply, sub-tract, sub-tract, She need - ed rules she
need your as - sis-tance," she cried. . . "In all math-e-mat-ics your
need your aid," she cried, she cried, "In all my work your
mf
mis - sion, in - t'rest, in-t'rest rates,And pro - fit, par - tial
pla - ces where 'twas found,'twas found,Of ways to sim - pli -
mul - ti - ply, sub-tract, sub-tract, She need - ed rules she
need your aid," she cried, she cried,"In all my work your
mf
mp
pay-ments and bonds,And ta-bles of measures and weights. . .
pay - ments,bonds, And meas - ures, weights, ta-bles of weights.
sim - pli - fy terms And dif - fi - cult squares to com-pound. . . .
fy her terms And dif - fi - cult squares to com-pound.
learned in her youth, A - rith-me-tic's knowledge ex-act. . . .
learned in youth, A - rith - me - tic's knowl-edge ex-act.
rules I shall use. For-give me my fol - ly and pride.". . .
rules I use. For-give my pride, fol - ly and pride."
mp
pay - ments,bonds,And meas - ures, weights, ta-bles of weights.
fy . . her terms And dif - fi - cult squares to compound.
learned in youth, A - rith - me - tic's knowledge ex - act.
rules I use. For-give my pride, fol - ly and pride."
mp

Tranquillo
LISZT
148
p
1. The set - ting sun (the sun) makes cool the night (the night); The
2. Her si - ren song (her song) will bring but woe (but woe) Up -
pp
1. Sun - set cools, cools the
2. Ah! her song brings but
dolce
dis-tant moun - tain re-flects the light. A-bove the Rhine, a
The mountain re-flects, re-flects the light. A-bove the Rhine, the Rhine, a
on the boat - man en-tranced be-low. With cliffs for - got, . . his
To boat-man en-tranced, entranced be - low. With cliffs for - got, for - got, his
night, cools the night. . . . . O'er the
woe far be - low. . . . . Cliffs for -
maid - en fair (so fair) With comb of gold smooths out her
boat and he (and he) Will find their grave be - neath the
Rhine sings a maid with
got, soon the boat - - - - - man
p espress. pp
hair, Her gold-en, gold - en hair. . . .
hair, her gold - en hair, Her gold - - en, gold - en hair. .
sea, Be - neath the cru - el sea. . . .
sea, be - neath the sea, Be - neath . . . . the cru - el sea. .
gold - en, gold - en hair, With gold - en, gold - en hair. . . . . .
sinks be - neath the sea, Be - neath . . the cru - el sea. . . . .

OUT ON THE DEEP

SAMUEL K. COWAN
FREDERIC N. LÖHR
Allegro moderato
mf
149
1. Out on the deep when the sun is low And the sea with
2. Out on the deep when the sun is dead And the first sweet
cres.
splen-dor burns, . With his sca - ly spoil from his
star doth gleam, . Of a day that is dead and a
mf
ev - 'ning toil The fish - er home-ward turns, . And his
love that is fled The fish - er oft will dream, . And he
cres.
oars flash bright in the o - cean light, And he knows that
thinks, though far, like that first bright star, She is still be -
f
eyes on shore Look out on the deep . for his
side as of yore, And his oars gleam bright in its
f
bright oar sweep, And he sings as he swings his oar: . "A
sweet pale light, And he sings as he plies his oar: . "A
long sweep, lads, and a strong sweep, boys, And a song as a -
slow sweep, lads, and a low sweep, boys, And a song as a -
cres.
long we go, . . For the hearts that yearn for our home re -
long we go, . . For the star of Love, that is bright a -

dim.
molto rall.
turn, When the ev - 'ning sun is low, . When the
bove, And its gleam in the wave be - low, . And its
mf a tempo
dim. poco a poco
ev - 'ning sun . . is low." . . . .
gleam in the wave . . be - low." . . . .
THE BELLS OF ABERDOVEY[1]
WALTER MAYNARD
Welsh Folk Song
Arr. by W. RHYS-HERBERT
Moderato
mf
150
1 In the peace-ful ev-'ning time, Oft I lis - ten to the chime,
2. When at morn I used to hear O'er the hills their voi - ces clear,
mf
1. In the peace-ful ev-'ning time, Oft I lis - ten to the chime,
2. When at morn I used to hear O'er the hills their voi - ces clear,
mf
1.2. "Bim, boom, Bim, boom,
rall.
a tempo
To the dul - cet, ring - ing rhyme, Of the bells of A - ber - do - vey.
They would then my young heart cheer, Those sweet bells of A - ber - do - vey.
rall.
a tempo
To the dul - cet, ring - ing rhyme, Of the bells of A - ber - do - vey.
They would then my young heart cheer, Those sweet bells of A - ber - do - vey.
rall.
a tempo
Bim, boom," . . Say the bells of A - ber - do - vey.

[1]To be sung by the three upper voices, or by the two upper voices and the bass.

p
pp
One, (one,) two, (two,) three, (three,) four, (four,) Hark! (hark!) they ring! Ah!
One, (one,) two, (two,) three, (three,) four, (four,) They (they) did sound, And
mp
pp
One, two, three, four, Hark! they ring! Ah!
One, two, three, four, They did sound, And
One, two, three, four, Hark! they ring! "Bim,
a tempo
rall.
pp a tempo
Fine
long-lost thoughts to me they bring, Those sweet bells of A - ber - do - vey.
then the e - choes would re - sound To the bells of A - ber - do - vey.
1–2. Peace is found in Heav'n a - lone," Say the bells of A - ber - do - vey.
long lost thoughts to me they bring, Those sweet bells of A - ber - do - vey.
then the e - choes would re - sound To the bells of A - ber - do - vey.
1–2. Peace is found in Heav'n a - lone," Say the bells of A - ber - do - vey.
bim, boom," . . Say the bells of A - ber - do - vey.
mf
I first heard them years a - go, When, care-less and light-heart-ed,
All their mu - sic seemed to me Full of loud mirth and pleas-ure,
Bim, bim, boom, Bim, bim, boom,
"Bim, boom, Bim, bim, boom,

mf *dim.*

I thought not of com - ing woe, Nor of bright days de - part - ed.
And I sang right mer - ri - ly, To its me - lo-dious meas - ure.

mp *dim.*

Bim, bim, boom, Bim, boom, bim, boom,

mp *dim.*

Bim, boom, Bim, boom, bim, boom,

rit. D.S.

Now these years are past and gone, "When the strife of life is done,

rit. D.S.

. . Bim, boom, ... Bim, boom.

rit. D.S.

. . Bim, boom, ... Bim, boom.

TRUTH TRIUMPHANT

RICHARD STRAUSS
Arr. by HARVEY WORTHINGTON LOOMIS

Slowly and peacefully

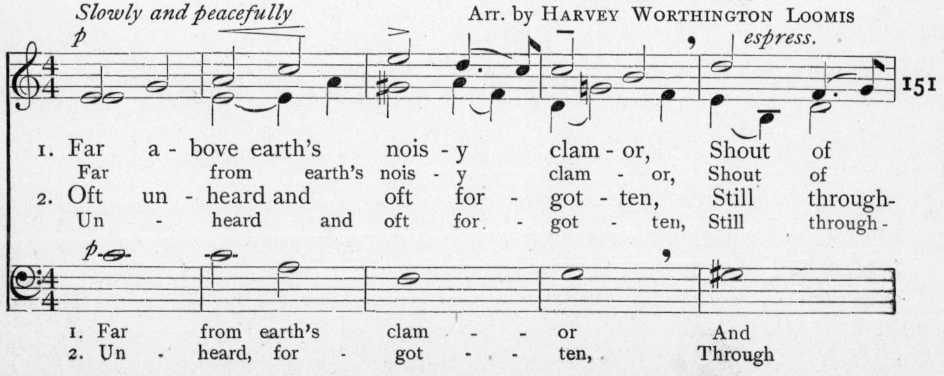

p
espress.
151
1. Far a - bove earth's nois - y clam - or, Shout of
Far from earth's nois - y clam - or, Shout of
2. Oft un - heard and oft for - got - ten, Still through-
Un - heard and oft for - got - ten, Still through -
p
1. Far from earth's clam - - - or And
2. Un - heard, for - got - - - ten, Through

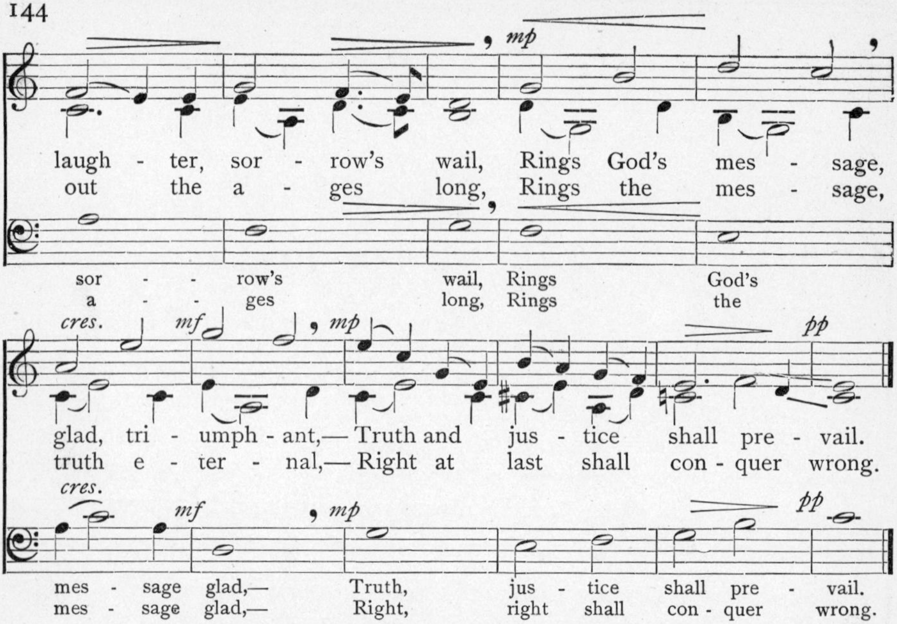

laugh - ter, sor - row's wail, Rings God's mes - sage,
out the a - ges long, Rings the mes - sage,

sor - - row's wail, Rings God's
a - - ges long, Rings the

glad, tri - umph - ant,— Truth and jus - tice shall pre - vail.
truth e - ter - nal,— Right at last shall con - quer wrong.

mes - sage glad,— Truth, jus - tice shall pre - vail.
mes - sage glad,— Right, right shall con - quer wrong.

THE STAR-SPANGLED BANNER

FRANCIS SCOTT KEY — JOHN STAFFORD SMITH

Con spirito

152 

1. Oh, say, can you see, by the dawn's ear - ly light, What so
2. On the shore, dim - ly seen thro' the mists of the deep, Where the
3. Oh, thus be it ev - er when free - men shall stand Be -

proud - ly we hail'd at the twi - light's last gleam - ing, Whose broad
foe's haugh-ty host in dread si - lence re - pos - es, What is
tween their lov'd homes and the war's des - o - la - tion; Blest with

stripes and bright stars thro' the per - il - ous fight, O'er the ram - parts we
that which the breeze o'er the tow - er - ing steep, As it fit - ful - ly
vic - t'ry and peace, may the heav'n-rescued land Praise the pow'r that hath

watched were so gal - lant - ly stream - ing? And the rock - ets' red
blows, half con-ceals, half dis - clos - es? Now it catch - es the
made and pre-serv'd us a na - tion! Then con - quer we

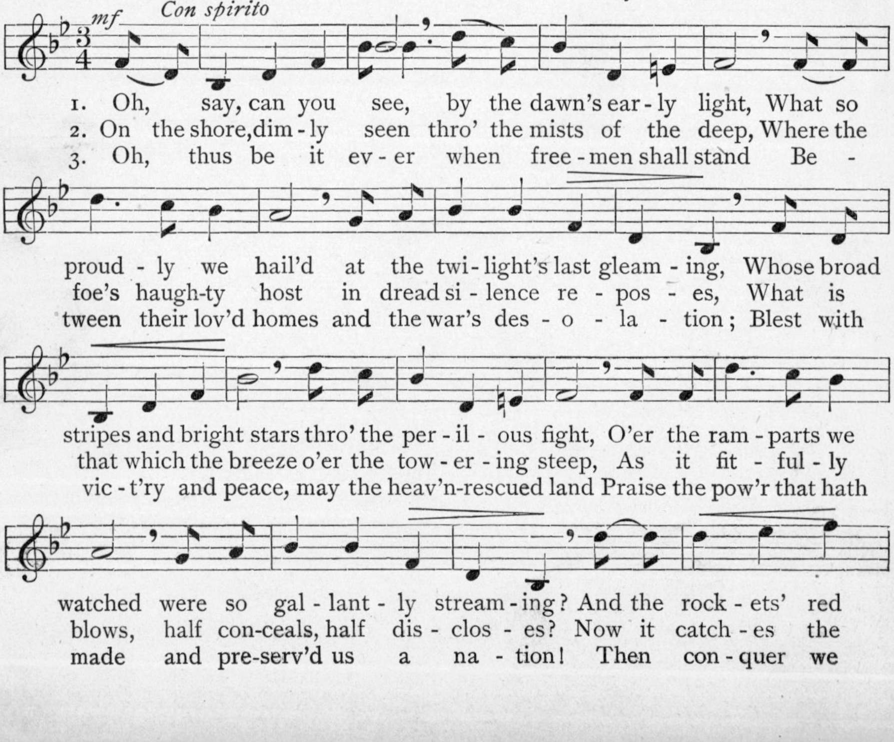

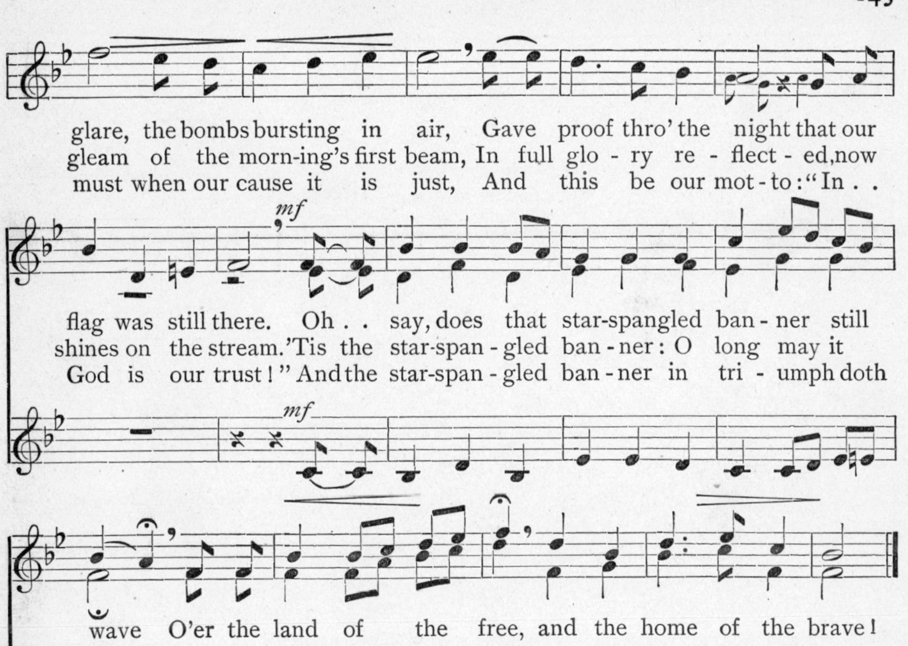
mf
glare, the bombs bursting in air, Gave proof thro' the night that our
gleam of the morn-ing's first beam, In full glo - ry re - flect - ed, now
must when our cause it is just, And this be our mot - to: "In . .
flag was still there. Oh . . say, does that star-spangled ban - ner still
shines on the stream. 'Tis the star-span - gled ban - ner: O long may it
God is our trust!" And the star-span - gled ban - ner in tri - umph doth
wave O'er the land of the free, and the home of the brave!

COLUMBIA, THE GEM OF THE OCEAN

DAVID F. SHAW | DAVID F. SHAW

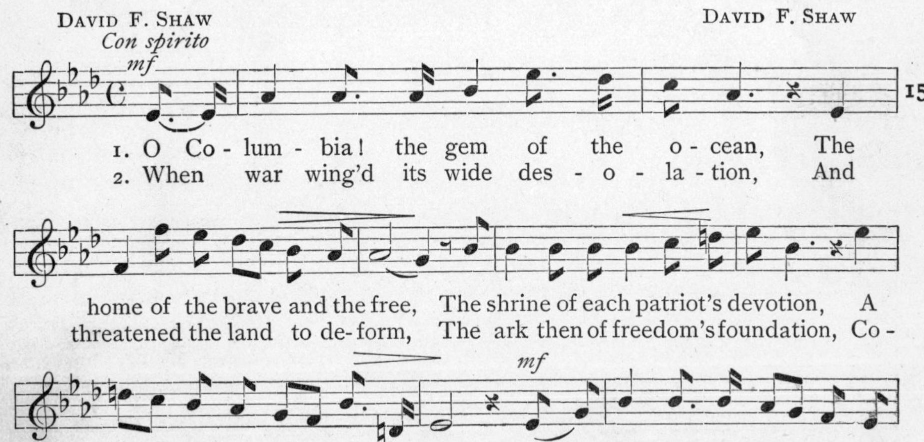
Con spirito
mf
153
1. O Co - lum - bia! the gem of the o - cean, The
2. When war wing'd its wide des - o - la - tion, And
home of the brave and the free, The shrine of each patriot's devotion, A
threatened the land to de - form, The ark then of freedom's foundation, Co -
world of - fers hom - age to thee! Thy man - dates make he - roes as -
lum - bia, rode safe thro' the storm: With the gar - lands of vic - t'ry a -

sem - ble, When Lib - er - ty's form stands in view; Thy
round her, When so proud - ly she bore her brave crew, With her
ban-ners make tyr - an - ny trem-ble, When borne by the red, white, and blue.
flag proud-ly float-ing be - fore her, The boast of the red, white, and blue.
mf
When borne by the red, white, and blue, When borne by the red, white, and
The boast of the red, white, and blue, The boast of the red, white, and
mf
When borne, when borne by the red, white, and blue, When borne, when borne by the
The boast, the boast of the red, white, and blue, The boast, the boast of the
blue, Thy ban - ners make tyr - an - ny
blue, With her flag proud - ly float - ing be -
red, white, and blue,
red, white, and blue,
trem - ble, When borne by the red, white, and blue.
fore her, The boast of the red, white, and blue.

HAIL, COLUMBIA!

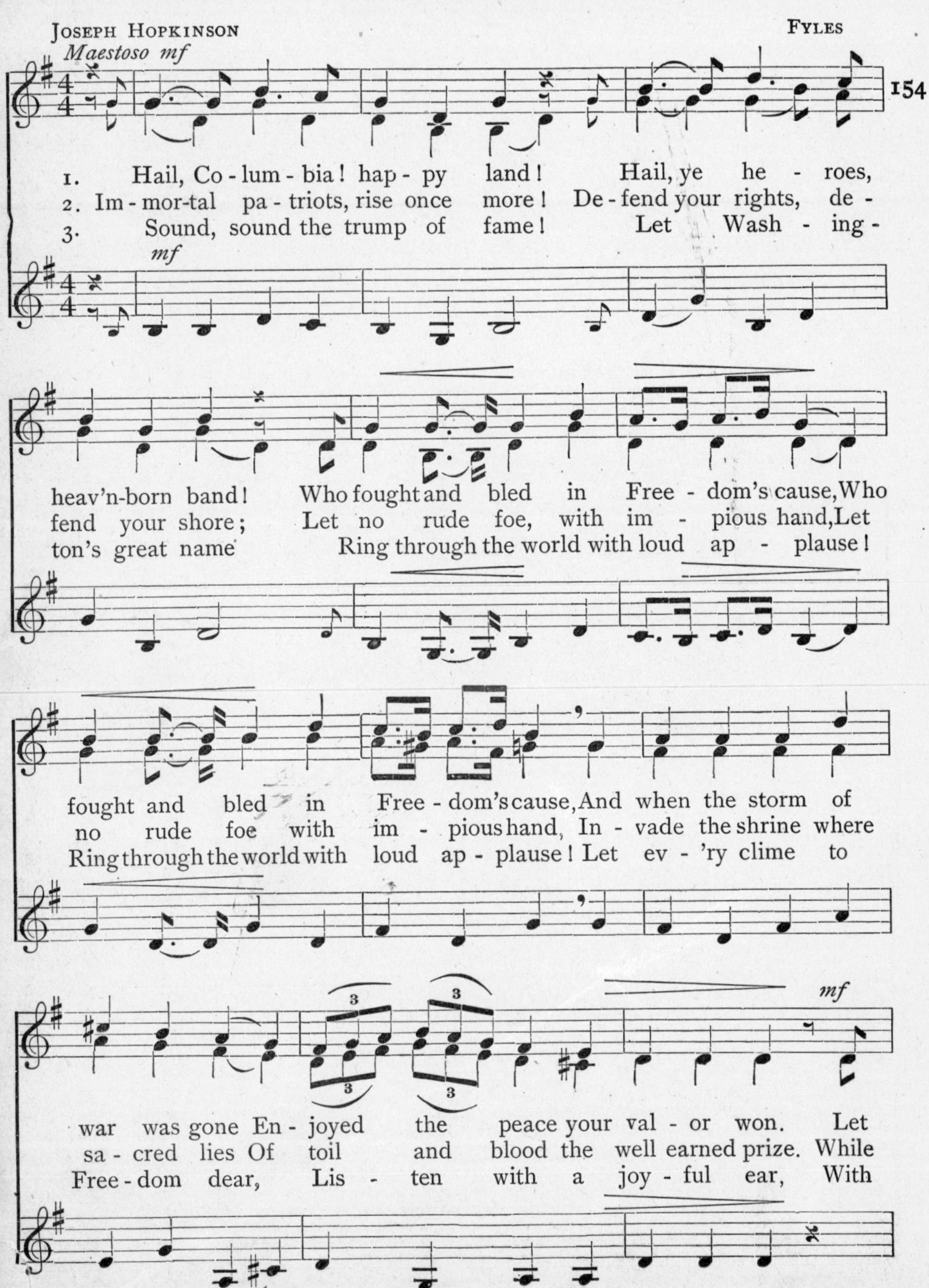
JOSEPH HOPKINSON
FYLES
Maestoso mf
154
1. Hail, Co - lum - bia! hap - py land! Hail, ye he - roes,
2. Im - mor-tal pa - triots, rise once more! De - fend your rights, de -
3. Sound, sound the trump of fame! Let Wash - ing -
mf
heav'n-born band! Who fought and bled in Free - dom's cause, Who
fend your shore; Let no rude foe, with im - pious hand, Let
ton's great name Ring through the world with loud ap - plause!
fought and bled in Free - dom's cause, And when the storm of
no rude foe with im - pious hand, In - vade the shrine where
Ring through the world with loud ap - plause! Let ev - 'ry clime to
war was gone En - joyed the peace your val - or won. Let
sa - cred lies Of toil and blood the well earned prize. While
Free - dom dear, Lis - ten with a joy - ful ear, With
mf
3

sempre marcato
mp
in - de - pend-ence be our boast, . . Ev - er mind - ful
of - f'ring peace, sin - cere and just, In heav'n we place a
e - qual skill, with stead-y pow'r, He gov - erns in the
mp
Let in - de-pend - ence be our boast, Ev - er mind-ful
While of-f'ring peace, sin - cere and just, In heav'n we place a
With e - qual skill, with stead-y pow'r, He gov - erns in the
mf
mp
what it cost, Ev - er grate - ful for the prize,
man - ly trust, That truth and jus - tice shall pre - vail, And
fear - ful hour Of hor - rid war, or guides with ease, The
mp
what it cost, Ev - er grate - ful for the prize,
man - ly trust, That truth and jus - tice shall pre - vail, And
fear - ful hour Of hor - rid war, or guides with ease, The
mf
Let its al - tar reach the skies. Firm, u - nit - ed, let us be,
ev - 'ry scheme of bond - age fail.
hap-pier time of hon - est peace.
mf
mf molto marcato
Ral - lying round our lib - er - ty! As a band of
mf molto marcato

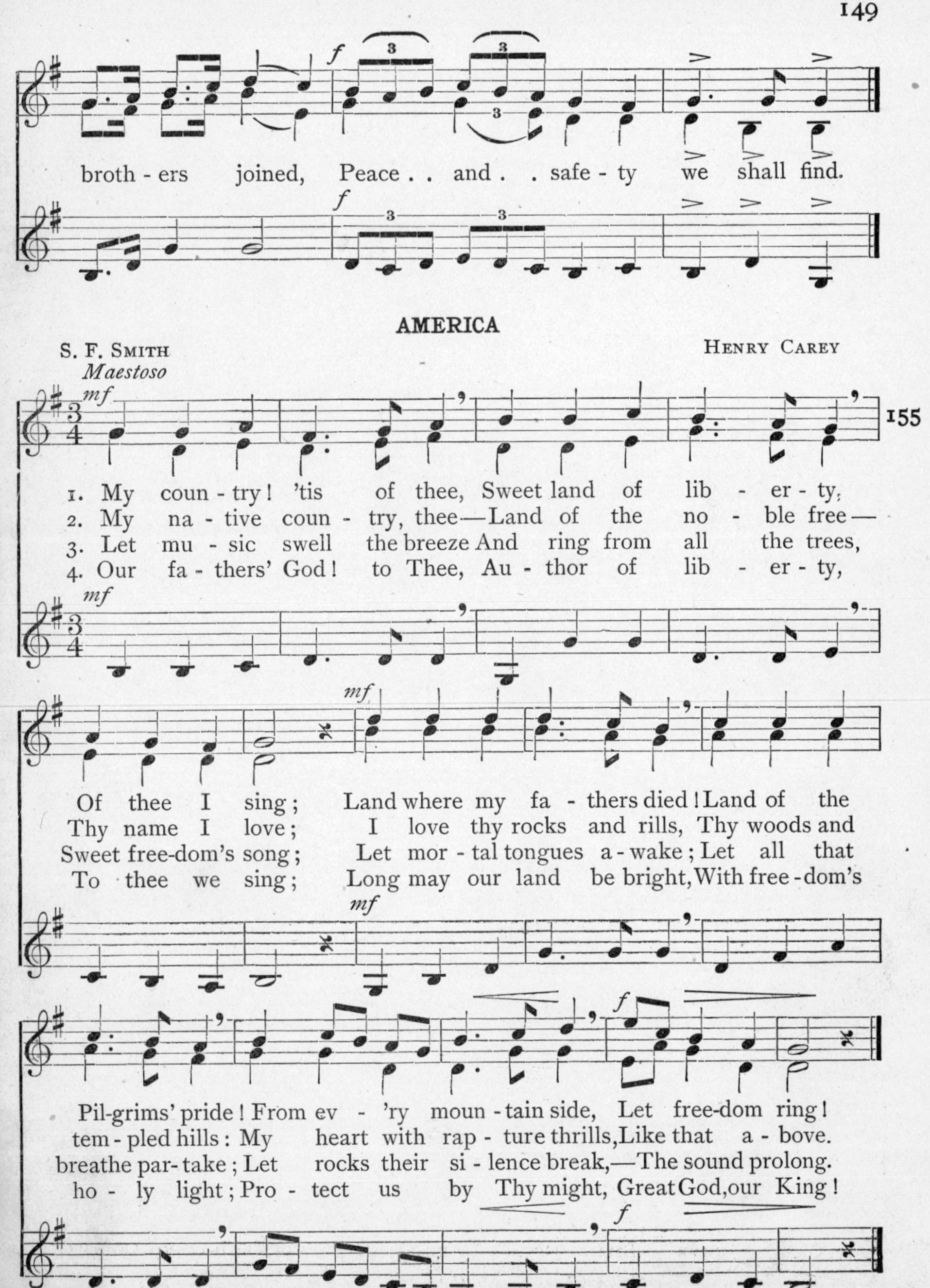

broth - ers joined, Peace . . and . . safe - ty we shall find.
AMERICA
S. F. SMITH
HENRY CAREY
Maestoso
155
1. My coun - try! 'tis of thee, Sweet land of lib - er - ty,
2. My na - tive coun - try, thee—Land of the no - ble free—
3. Let mu - sic swell the breeze And ring from all the trees,
4. Our fa - thers' God! to Thee, Au - thor of lib - er - ty,
Of thee I sing; Land where my fa - thers died! Land of the
Thy name I love; I love thy rocks and rills, Thy woods and
Sweet free-dom's song; Let mor - tal tongues a - wake; Let all that
To thee we sing; Long may our land be bright, With free - dom's
Pil-grims' pride! From ev - 'ry moun - tain side, Let free-dom ring!
tem - pled hills: My heart with rap - ture thrills, Like that a - bove.
breathe par - take; Let rocks their si - lence break,—The sound prolong.
ho - ly light; Pro - tect us by Thy might, Great God, our King!

GLOSSARY

TERMS OF NOTATION

1 **Staff,**— five horizontal lines and four equal spaces.

2 **Leger Lines, or Added Lines,** —light lines below and above the staff.

3 **A, B, C, D, E, F, G, — Pitches,**— the first seven letters of the alphabet by which tones are designated.

4 **G Clef,**— fixes G upon the second line, around which it turns. The staff thus marked is called the treble staff.

5 **F Clef,** — fixes F upon the fourth line, around which it turns. The staff thus marked is called the bass staff.

6 **The Great Staff,**— the combined treble and bass staves, formerly written as an eleven-line staff.

To distinguish between pitches in different octaves, the following distinction is made; great octave, small octave, one-lined octave, two-lined octave.

C (great c) the c on the second line below the bass staff.

c (small c) the c in the second space of the bass staff.

c̄ (one-lined c) the c on the first leger line above the bass staff and on the first leger line below the treble staff.

c̿ (two-lined c) the c in the third space of the treble staff.

7 **Bars,**— vertical lines upon the staff.

A Bar is one vertical line.

A Double Bar is two vertical lines and sometimes a *thick* vertical line.

8 **A Measure,** — the space between two bars, representing a group of strong and weak beats.

9 **Brace,**— a vertical line which joins two or more staves.

10 **Notes:**—

a) **Whole-note,** — an open note-head without stem.

b) **Half-note,** — an open note-head with stem.

c) **Quarter-note,** — a closed note-head with stem.

d) **Eighth-note,** — a closed note-head with stem and *one* hook.

e) **Sixteenth-note,** — a closed note-head with stem and *two* hooks.

f) **Thirty-second-note,**— a closed note-head with stem and *three* hooks.

g) **Grace-note,**—a small note with or without a stroke across the stem, representing a passing tone preceding an essential tone, and borrowing the time it occupies from the essential tone.

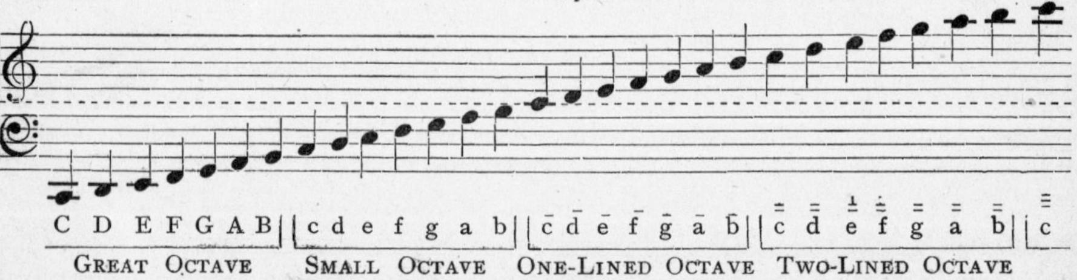

C D E F G A B
c d e f g a b
c̄ d̄ ē f̄ ḡ ā b̄
c̿ d̿ e̿ f̿ g̿ a̿ b̿
c
GREAT OCTAVE
SMALL OCTAVE
ONE-LINED OCTAVE
TWO-LINED OCTAVE

11 Rests: —

a) ▬ **Whole-rest.**

b) ▬ **Half-rest.**

c) 𝄽 **Quarter-rest.**

d) 𝄾 **Eighth-rest.**

e) 𝄿 **Sixteenth-rest.**

1 **The Tie,** — a curved line joining two notes of the *same* pitch.

It indicates that the second note over or under the tie is not to be repeated, but *sustained*, joined with the first.

13 (·) **The Dot,** — placed after a note lengthens it one-half; thus the dot after a half-note takes the place of a *quarter-note tied.*

The dot after a quarter-note takes the place of an *eighth-note tied.*

The dot after an *eighth-note* takes the place of a *sixteenth-note* tied.

The dot after a rest lengthens it one-half; thus the dot after a half-rest takes the place of a quarter-rest.

The dot after a quarter-rest takes the place of an eighth-rest.

The dot after an eighth-rest takes the place of a sixteenth-rest.

14 (· ·) **The Double Dot,** — placed after a note or a rest lengthens its duration three-fourths; thus the double dot after a half-note takes the place of a quarter-note and an eighth-note tied.

The double dot after a quarter-note takes the place of an eighth-note and a sixteenth-note tied.

15 The Phrase Mark,—a curved line indicating the rhythmical grouping of notes.

16 **Breath Mark,** — a comma placed above the staff to suggest a place for taking breath.

17 **The Slur,** — a curved line joining two or more notes of *different* pitch.

It indicates that the notes so joined are to be sung to one syllable.

18 **The Hold or Pause,** — a dot under or over a small curved line. It means that the note or rest over or under which it is placed is to be held longer than usual.

19

Staccato Marks,— direct that the tones be distinct, separated from each other. The wedge-shaped marks are the most emphatic staccato signs; dots over or under the notes with a sweeping curve mark the slightest staccato. The latter effect is called *non legato.*

20 **The Repeat,** — dots immediately before or after a bar. It indicates that music before or after the dots should be repeated.

21 **1st and 2d Endings,**—signs indicating that, in the repetition, the music marked *2d time* must be substituted for that under the sign *1st time.*

1st time *2d time*

22 *D.C.* **Da Capo,**—from the beginning (repeat).

23 *D.S.* **Dal Segno,** — from the sign :𝄋: (repeat).

24 **Al Fine,**— to the end.

25 **Coda,** — a passage at the end of a musical composition added to make a more effective conclusion.

26 **Characters affecting Pitch:** —

a) ♯ **The Sharp,**—raises the pitch represented by a staff-degree a half-step.

b) × **The Double-sharp,** — raises the pitch represented by a sharped staff-degree a half-step.

c) ♭ **The Flat,** — lowers the pitch represented by a staff-degree a half-step.

d) ♭♭ **The Double-flat,**— lowers the pitch represented by a flatted staff-degree a half-step.

e) ♮ **The Natural,** or **Cancel,**— removes the effect of a sharp or flat;

♮♭ removes the effect of one of the two flats in ♭♭;

♮♯ removes the effect of one of the two sharps in ×.

27 **Interval,** — the difference in pitch between two tones.

28 **Half-Step,**— the smallest interval employed in modern music.

29 **Step,** — an interval of two half-steps.

30 **Staff-Degrees,** — lines and spaces of the staff.

31 **Major Third,**— an interval embracing three staff-degrees and containing four half-steps.

32 **Minor Third,**— an interval embracing three staff-degrees and containing three half-steps.

33 **Mode,** — classification depending upon the sequence of steps and half-steps in scales. The modes in common use are the major and minor.

34 **Major Mode,**—the species of scale in which the third from the key-note is a major third.

35 **Minor Mode,**—the species of scale in which the third from the key-note is a minor third.

36 **Scale,** — a succession of tones within the octave, ascending or descending according to a fixed rule.

37 **The Major Scale,** — a succession of five steps and two half-steps in the following order: 1 to 2, a step; 2 to 3, a step; 3 to 4, a half-step; 4 to 5, a step; 5 to 6, a step; 6 to 7, a step; 7 to 8, a half-step. A major scale is a scale whose first third is a major third. (For scale building and development of signatures, see Glossary of the Second Music Reader.)

8
HALF-STEP
7
STEP
6
STEP

STEP
4
HALF-STEP
3
STEP
2
STEP
1

38 **The Chromatic Scale,**—twelve tones within the octave, ascending or descending in regular succession by half-steps. (For representation see Glossary of the Third Reader.)

39 **The Minor Scale,**—a scale whose first third is a minor third.

40 **Diagrams representing various forms of the Minor Scale:—**

	MINOR SCALE. Natural Form.	MAJOR SCALE.	MINOR SCALE. Harmonic Form.	
		8		
		7		
8th Degree.	6	6	6	8th
			♯5	7th
7th Degree.	5	5	- - - -	
6th Degree.	4	4	4	6th
5th Degree.	3	3	3	5th
4th Degree.	2	2	2	4th
3rd Degree.	1	1	1	3rd
2nd Degree.	7	7	7	2nd
1st Degree.	6	6	6	1st

MINOR SCALE DEGREES.

	MINOR SCALE. Melodic Form, Ascending.	MAJOR SCALE.	MINOR SCALE. Melodic Form, Descending.	
		8		
		7		
8th	6	6	6	8th Degree.
7th	♯5			
		5	5	7th Degree.
6th	♮4			
		4	4	6th Degree.
5th	3	3	3	5th Degree.
4th	2	2	2	4th Degree.
3rd	1	1	1	3rd Degree.
2nd	7	7	7	2nd Degree.
1st	6	6	6	1st Degree.

41 **Major Scales and Their Relative Minor Scales, Melodic Form:—**

Scale of C Major and the Relative A Minor, Melodic Form

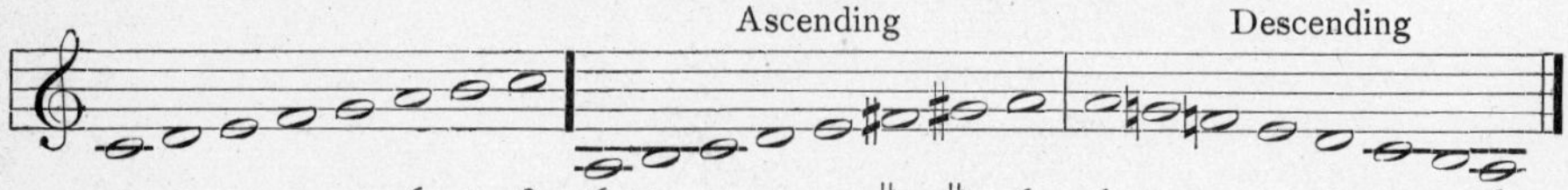

Ascending Descending

1 2 3 4 5 6 7 8 6 7 1 2 3 ♯4 ♯5 6 6 5 4 3 2 1 7 6

Scale of G Major and the Relative E Minor, Melodic Form

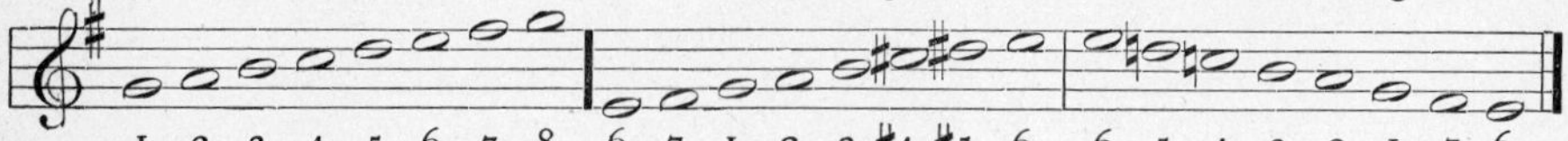

Ascending Descending

1 2 3 4 5 6 7 8 6 7 1 2 3 ♯4 ♯5 6 6 5 4 3 2 1 7 6

Scale of D Major and the Relative B Minor, Melodic Form

Ascending Descending

1 2 3 4 5 6 7 8 6 7 1 2 3 ♯4 ♯5 6 6 5 4 3 2 1 7 6

Scale of A Major and the Relative F♯ Minor, Melodic Form

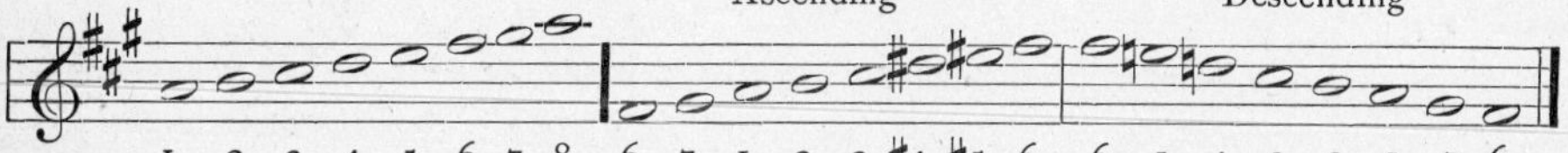

Ascending Descending

1 2 3 4 5 6 7 8 6 7 1 2 3 ♯4 ♯5 6 6 5 4 3 2 1 7 6

Scale of E Major and the Relative C♯ Minor, Melodic Form

Ascending Descending

1 2 3 4 5 6 7 8 6 7 1 2 3 ♯4 ♯5 6 6 5 4 3 2 1 7 6

Scale of B Major and the Relative G♯ Minor, Melodic Form

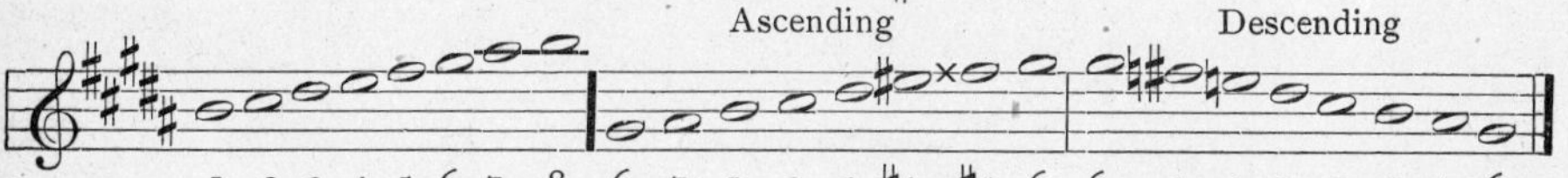

Ascending Descending

1 2 3 4 5 6 7 8 6 7 1 2 3 ♯4 ♯5 6 6 5 4 3 2 1 7 6

Scale of F♯ Major and the Relative D♯ Minor, Melodic Form

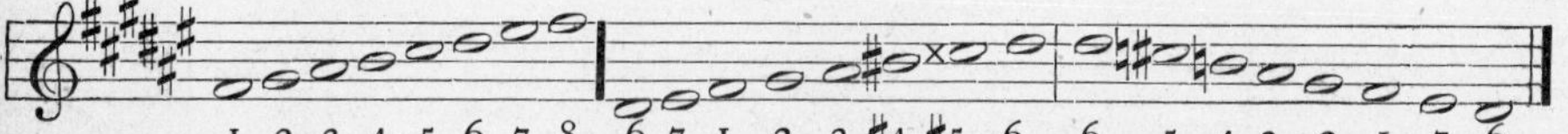

Ascending Descending

1 2 3 4 5 6 7 8 6 7 1 2 3 ♯4 ♯5 6 6 5 4 3 2 1 7 6

Major Scales and Their Relative Minor Scales, Melodic Form, continued: —

Scale of C♯ Major and the Relative A♯ Minor, Melodic Form
Ascending
Descending
1 2 3 4 5 6 7 8 6 7 1 2 3 ♯4 ♯5 6 6 5 4 3 2 1 7 6
Scale of F Major and the Relative D Minor, Melodic Form
Ascending
Descending
1 2 3 4 5 6 7 8 6 7 1 2 3 ♯4 ♯5 6 6 5 4 3 2 1 7 6
Scale of B♭ Major and the Relative G Minor, Melodic Form
Ascending
Descending
1 2 3 4 5 6 7 8 6 7 1 2 3 ♯4 ♯5 6 6 5 4 3 2 1 7 6
Scale of E♭ Major and the Relative C Minor, Melodic Form
Ascending
Descending
1 2 3 4 5 6 7 8 6 7 1 2 3 ♯4 ♯5 6 6 5 4 3 2 1 7 6
Scale of A♭ Major and the Relative F Minor, Melodic Form
Ascending
Descending
1 2 3 4 5 6 7 8 6 7 1 2 3 ♯4 ♯5 6 6 5 4 3 2 1 7 6
Scale of D♭ Major and the Relative B♭ Minor, Melodic Form
Ascending
Descending
1 2 3 4 5 6 7 8 6 7 1 2 3 ♯4 ♯5 6 6 5 4 3 2 1 7 6
Scale of G♭ Major and the Relative E♭ Minor, Melodic Form
Ascending
Descending
1 2 3 4 5 6 7 8 6 7 1 2 3 ♯4 ♯5 6 6 5 4 3 2 1 7 6
Scale of C♭ Major and the Relative A♭ Minor, Melodic Form
Ascending
Descending
1 2 3 4 5 6 7 8 6 7 1 2 3 ♯4 ♯5 6 6 5 4 3 2 1 7 6

42 **The Circle of Keys,**— an arrangement of keys or tonalities in the order of their closest relationship — that is, each key-note being the dominant (over-fifth), or subdominant (fourth or under-fifth) of the one before it.

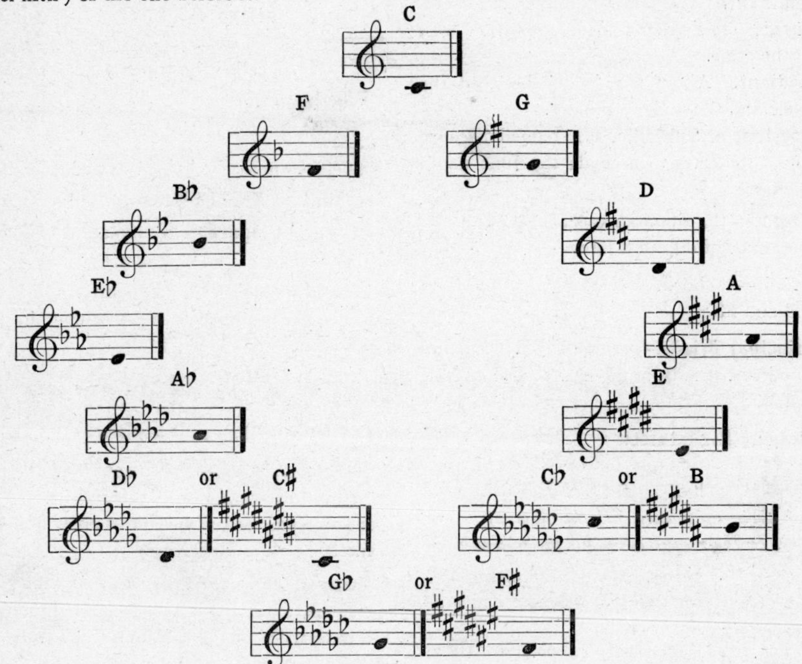
C
F
G
B♭
D
E♭
A
A♭
E
D♭ or C♯
C♭ or B
G♭ or F♯

The circle may be made in either direction from the key of C by making the necessary enharmonic change at one of the three possible points.

43 **Transition,** — passing suddenly out of one key into another. The part of the signature which does not appear in the new key is cancelled just before the heavy bar marking the close of the first key; thus, —

Transition from the key whose signature is four flats to the key whose signature is one flat.

44 **Scale Names,**— One, Two, Three, Four, Five, Six, Seven, and Eight,— the names applied to the successive tones of the major scale.

45 **Intermediate Tones,**— Sharp-one, Sharp-two, Sharp-four, Sharp-five, and Sharp-six,— the intermediate tones which may be introduced into the scale ascending. Flat-seven, Flat-six, Flat-five, Flat-three and Flat-two,—the intermediate tones which may be introduced into the scale descending.

46 **Syllables,**— commonly sung to the successive tones of the scale: 1, do; 2, re; 3, mi; 4, fa; 5, sol; 6, la; 7, ti (or si); 8, do. Intermediate syllables ascending,— ♯1, di; ♯2, ri; ♯4, fi; ♯5, si (or sil); ♯6, li: descending,— ♭7, te (or se); ♭6, le; ♭5, se (or sel); ♭3, me; ♭2, ra.

47 **Scale-Degrees,**— names applied to the successive degrees of the scale, major or minor: 1st degree, Tonic; 2d degree, Supertonic; 3d degree, Mediant; 4th degree, Subdominant; 5th degree, Dominant; 6th degree, Submediant; 7th degree, Leading-tone or Subtonic.

Tonic. Most important tone in the scale.

Supertonic. Tone "above the tonic."

Mediant. About "midway" between the tonic and dominant.

Subdominant. The lower or under dominant.

Dominant. The second most important tone in the scale.

Submediant. About "midway" between the tonic and the underdominant.

Leading-tone or Subtonic. So named because of its tendency to ascend; the tone under the tonic.

48 **Chord,**— the simultaneous sounding of two or more tones of different pitch.

49 **Triad,**—a chord consisting of a tone with its third and fifth.

50 **Principal Triads,**— the tonic, subdominant, and dominant triads, numbered respectively I, IV, and V.

51 **Measure-Signatures:** —

$\frac{2}{4}$, $\frac{2}{2}$ two-quarter measure and two-half measure; i. e., two quarter *notes or their equivalent fill the* measure: two half *notes or their equivalent fill the* measure.

₵ barred C, used interchangeably for two-half measure and four-half measure.

$\frac{3}{8}$, $\frac{3}{4}$, $\frac{3}{2}$ three-eighth measure, three-quarter measure, and three-half measure.

$\frac{4}{4}$, C four-quarter measure.

$\frac{6}{8}$, $\frac{6}{4}$ six-eighth measure and six-quarter measure.

$\frac{9}{8}$ $\frac{12}{8}$ nine-eighth measure and twelve-eighth measure.

52 **Beat,** — pulse; an equal division of the measure.

53 **Rhythmic Type,** — time values equal to a beat. When the quarter-note is the beat unit, the rhythmic types are:

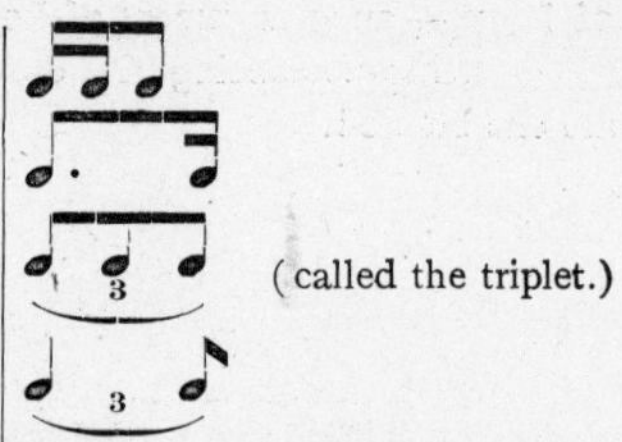
3
3

(called the triplet.)

The eighth-note, the half-note, and sometimes other notes are used as the beat unit.

54 **Rhythmic figure,** — combination of rhythmic types: thus, is a rhythmic figure equal to two beats, when the quarter-note is the beat-unit. Rhythm varies according to the rhythmic types included; thus

$\frac{3}{4}$ and $\frac{3}{4}$ differ in rhythm while they coincide in measure.

55 **Syncopation,** — an interruption of the natural pulsation of the music, bringing the strong accent on a part of the measure usually not thus accented.

56 **Bass ad lib.,** — literally bass "at will"; i.e., the bass may be sung or omitted at discretion. The bass voice is not absolutely essential to complete harmonic setting.

57 **A B** etc.,— reference letters used as a mechanical convenience in referring to movements or divisions of the music.

58 **Cantata,** — a short musical work consisting of choruses and solos, with instrumental accompaniment. It may be sacred or secular.

59 **Chorus,**—music sung by many voices in unison or in parts.

60 **Duet,**—a two-part musical composition each part of which is equally important in melody—that is, contrapuntal.

61 **Folk Song,**—a song whose words and music have originated among the people.

62 **Folk Tune,**— a melody which has originated among the people.

63 **Incidental Music,** — vocal or instrumental music performed during the action or speech of a play.

64 **Opera,** — a drama or play set to music.

Comic Opera, — an opera made up entirely of gayety and farce.

Grand Opera, — a serious opera in which there is no spoken dialogue.

Opera Comique, — an opera with spoken dialogue.

Romantic opera, — in form similar to *opera comique*; the subject, a fairy tale treated seriously.

65 **Oratorio,** — a large musical work with text founded upon scriptural narrative, performed without scenery and action.

66 **Part Song,** — a composition of three or more parts in which the lower parts serve merely as an accompaniment.

67 **Rondo,** — a round of tunes in related keys.

68 **Solo,** — to be sung by a single voice.

69 **Sonata,** — a large musical composition in several separate parts or movements.

70 **Symphony,** — a sonata written for the orchestra.

71 **Three-part Song,**—song arranged for three voices.

72 **Trio,** — a three-part composition.

TERMS AND SIGNS OF EXPRESSION[1]

Accelerando (ȧt-chā-lā-rän′dō), accelerating.
Adagio (ȧ-dä′jō), slow ; literally, at leisure.
Alla burla (ȧl′lȧ bo͞or′lȧ), humorously.
Alla marcia (ȧl′lȧ mär′chiȧ), in the manner of a march.
Allegretto (äl-lā-grāt′tō), less quick than *allegro;* diminutive of *allegro.*
Allegro (äl-lā′grō), quick, lively; literally, cheerful.
Andante (än-dän′tā), slow, graceful ; moving at a moderate pace ; literally, walking.
Andantino (än-dän-tē′nō), the diminutive of *andante* and indicating here quicker *tempo.*
Animato (ȧ-nē-mä′tō), animated.
Assai (äs-sä′ē), very.
A tempo (ä tĕm′pō), return to first rate of speed.
Ben marcato (bĕn mär-kä′tō), well marked.
Cantabile (kȧn-tä′bē-lā), in a singing style, or very *legato.*
Commodo (kŏm′mō-dō) } with ease.
Comodo (kō′mō-dō) }
Con anima (kōn ä′nē-mä), with animation.
Con brio (kōn brē′ō), with vigor, spirit, force.
Con espressione (kōn ās-prās-sē-ō′nā), with expression.
Con grazia (kōn grä′tsē-ȧ), with grace.
Con moto (kōn mō′tō), with spirited movement.
Con moto di barcarolla (kōn mō′tō dē bär′kȧ-rō′lȧ), with the movement of a boating song.
Con moto di schottische (kōn mō′tō dē shŏt′-tĭsh), with the movement of a schottishe.
Con spirito (kōn spē′rē-tō), with spirit, energy.
Con tenerezza (kōn tān-ā-rāt′sȧ), with tenderness.
< **Crescendo** (krā-shān′dō), gradually increasing the tone.
> **Diminuendo** (dē-mē-no͞o-ān′dō), gradually lessening the tone.
Dolce (dŏl′chā), sweet, soft.
Espressivo (ās-prās-sē′vō), with expression.
f, forte (fôr′tā), loud.
ff, fortissimo (fôr-tēs′sē-mō), very loud.
Giocoso (jō-kō′sō), humorous, playful.
Giojoso (jō-yō′sō), joyous.
Giusto (jo͞os′tō), in just, exact time.
Grazioso (grä-tsē-ō′sō), graceful, elegant.
Larghetto (lär-gāt′tō), rather slow; the diminutive of *largo,* which means slow, or, literally, large.
Largo (lär′gō), slow, broad.
Legato (lā-gä′tō), even, continuous, flowing; literally, tied.
Leggiero (lād-jē-ā′rō), light.
Lento (lān′tō), literally, slow.
Lusingando (lo͞o′zēn-gän′dō), coaxingly, persuasively.
Ma (mä), but.
Maestoso (mä-ĕs-tō′zō), with dignity, majesty.
Marcato (mär-kä′tō), distinct, emphasized; literally, marked.
Marcia (mär′chiȧ), march.
Marziale (mär-tsē-ä′lā), martial, in the style of a march.
Meno (mā′nō), less.
Meno mosso (mā′nō mŏs′sō), less speed, less fast.
mf, mezzo forte (mĕd′zō fôr′tā), half loud.
Misterioso (mēs-tā-rē-ō′sō), mysterious.
Moderato (mŏd-ĕ-rä′tō), moderate.
Molto (mōl′tō), much, very.
mp, mezzo piano (mĕd′zō pē-ä′nō), half soft.
Non troppo (nōn trŏp′pō), not too much.
p, piano (pē-ä′nō), soft.
Pensieroso (pĕn-sĕ-ē-rō′sō), thoughtful, pensive.
Più (pē′ụ), a little more.
Poco più moto (pō′kō pē′ụ mō′tō), somewhat faster.
pp, pianissimo (pē′ȧ-nĭs′sĭ-mō), very soft.
Presto (prĕs′tō), fast, in rapid *tempo;* usually one beat to the measure; literally, quick.
Rallentando (räl-lĕn-tän′dō), becoming slower; literally, abating. Abb. *rall.*
Religioso (rā-lē-jō′sō), solemn, devout.
Rinf., rinforzando (rĭn-fôr-tsän′dō), suddenly emphasized and accented.
Risoluto (rē-zō-lo͞o′tō), energetic, decided.
Ritardando (rē′tär-dän′dō), slower; literally, retarding. Abb. *rit.*
Scherzando (skĕr-tsän′dō), sportive, playful.
Semplice (sĕm′plē-chā), simple.
Sempre (sĕm′prā), always, continually.
Sforzando (sfôr-tsän′dō) (>), with special emphasis.
Solennelle (sō-lĕn-nĕl′), solemn.
Sostenuto (sōs-tā-no͞o′tō), sustained.
Spiritoso (spē-rē-tō′sō), spirited.
Tanto (tän′tō), as much, so much.
Tempo di valse (tĕm′pō dē väl′sā), in the time of a waltz.
Tranquillo (trän-kwēl′lō), tranquil, quiet.
Veloce (vā-lō′chā), swiftly.
Vivace (vē-vä′chā), gay; literally, lively.
Vivo (vē′vō), animated.

[1] Webster's dictionary symbols of pronunciation used throughout.

INDEX TO GLOSSARY

No.

A 3
A. B. 57
Added lines 2
A-flat major, Scale of . . 41
A-flat minor, Scale of . . . 41
Al fine 24
A major, Scale of 41
A minor, Scale of 41
A-sharp minor, Scale of. 41

B 3
Bar 7
Barred C 51
Bass ad lib. 56
Beat 52
B-flat major, Scale of . . . 41
B-flat minor, Scale of . . . 41
B major, Scale of 41
B minor, Scale of 41
Brace 9
Breath mark 16

C 3
₵ 51
Cancel 26
Cantata 58
C c $\bar{c}$ $\bar{\bar{c}}$ 6
C-flat major, Key of 41
Characters affecting pitch 26
Chord 48
Chorus 59
Chromatic scale 38
Circle of keys 42
Clef 4
C major, Scale of 41
C minor, Scale of 41
Coda 25
Comic opera 64
C-sharp major, Scale of . 41
C-sharp minor, Scale of . 41

No.

D 3
Da capo 22
Dal segno 23
Degrees, Scale- 47
Degrees, Staff- 30
D-flat major, Scale of . . 41
Diagrams representing various forms of the minor scale 40
D major, Scale of 41
D minor, Scale of 41
Dominant 47
Dot 13
Double bar 7
Double dot 14
Double-flat 26
Double-sharp 26
D-sharp minor, Scale of. 41
Duet 60

E 3
E-flat major, Scale of . . . 41
E-flat minor, Scale of . . . 41
Eighth-note 10
Eighth-rest 11
E major, Scale of 41
E minor, Scale of 41

F 3
F clef 5
First and second endings 21
Flat 26
F major, Scale of 41
F minor, Scale of 41
Folk song 61
Folk tune 62
Four-quarter measure . . . 51
F-sharp major, Scale of. 41
F-sharp minor, Scale of . 41

No.

G 3
G clef 4
G-flat major, Scale of . . . 41
G major, Scale of 41
G minor, Scale of 41
Grace note 10
Grand opera 64
Great c (C) 6
Great octave 6
Great staff 6
G-sharp minor, Scale of . 41

Half-note 10
Half-rest 11
Half-step 28
Harmonic form of the minor scale 40
Hold 18

Incidental music 63
Intermediate tones 45
Interval 27

Leading-tone 47
Leger lines 2

Major mode 34
Major scale 37
Major scales and their relative minor scales . . . 41
Major third 31
Measure 8
Mediant 47
Melodic form of the minor scale 40
Minor mode 35
Minor scale 39
Minor third 32
Mode 33

	No.
Names, Scale	44
Natural	26
Natural form of the minor scale	40
Nine-eighth measure	51
Non legato	19
Notes	10
One-lined c ($\bar{c}$)	6
One-lined octave	6
Opera	64
Opera comique	64
Oratorio	65
Part song	66
Pause	18
Phrase mark	15
Pitches	3
Principal triads	50
Pulse	52
Quarter-note	10
Quarter-rest	11
Repeat	20
Rests	11
Rhythmic figure	54
Rhythmic type	53
Romantic opera	64
Rondo	67
Scale	36
Scale-degrees	47
Scale names	44
Sharp	26
Signatures, Measure-	51
Six-eighth measure	51
Six-quarter measure	51
Sixteenth-note	10
Sixteenth-rest	11
Slur	17
Small c (c)	6
Small octave	6
Solo	68
Sonata	69
Staccato marks	19
Staff	1
Staff-degrees	30
Step	29
Sub-dominant	47
Sub-mediant	47
Sub-tonic	47
Supertonic	47
Syllables	46
Symphony	70
Syncopation	55
Third, Major	31
Third, Minor	32
Thirty-second note	10
Three-eighth measure	51
Three-half measure	51
Three-part song	71
Three-quarter measure	51
Tie	12
Tonic	47
Transition	43
Triad	49
Triads, Principal	50
Trio	72
Triplet	53
Twelve-eighth measure	51
Two-half measure	51
Two-lined c ($\bar{\bar{c}}$)	6
Two-lined octave	6
Two-quarter measure	51
Whole-note	10
Whole-rest	11

INDEX TO SONGS

TITLE	AUTHOR	COMPOSER	PAGE
Abide With Me	Henry F. Lyte	*William H. Monk*	116
Alleluia	Francis Pott	*Palestrina*	135
Almighty Power	H. K. White	*Rossini*	90
America	S. F. Smith	*Henry Carey*	149
American Hymn		*M. Keller*	102
At Parting		*Harvey Worthington Loomis*	127
Austrian National Hymn		*Haydn*	83
Autumn Woods	Nixon Waterman	*A. S. Sullivan*	2
Believe Me, If All Those Endearing Young Charms	Thomas Moore	*Irish Folk Song*	131
Bells of Aberdovey	Walter Maynard	*Welsh Folk Song*	141
Brook, The	Alfred Tennyson	*H. Clough-Leighter*	106
Christmas	Nixon Waterman	*Ciro Pinsuti*	72
Closing Hymn	James Edmeston	*G. C. Stebbins*	34
Closing Year, The	M. B. Willis	*Schubert*	124
Columbia, the Gem of the Ocean	David T. Shaw	*David T. Shaw*	145
Come Unto Him		*Händel*	111
Dancing of Long Ago		*Mozart*	130
Dewey Dell, The	Alfred Waymark	*Henry Smart*	5
Discontented Pronoun, The	M. B. Willis	*Henry K. Hadley*	84
Dixie		*Dan Emmett*	88
Dream, The	Abbie Farwell Brown	*Gaetano Donizetti*	58
Evening Song	Abbie Farwell Brown	*Mozart*	16
Flight of the Birds	M. B. Willis	*Beethoven*	63
Fling Wide the Door		*Ciro Pinsuti*	28
Foot Ball Song, A		*English Folk Tune*	10
Four Seasons, The	M. B. Willis	*Haydn*	32
Graduation Song	M. A. L. Lane	*Ludwig Spohr*	67
Hail, Columbia!	Joseph Hopkinson	*Fyles*	147
Homeward Bound	Louis C. Elson	*Harvey Worthington Loomis*	1
Hungarian Lullaby		*Hungarian Folk Tune*	66
Hymn of Thanksgiving	John G. Whittier	*J. B. Calkin*	123
Hymn to Our Country	Belle Ames	*German Folk Tune*	35
I Wonder	M. B. Willis	*M. White*	114
I Waited for the Lord		*Mendelssohn*	78
In the Mountains	Tyrolean	*Thomas Koschat*	16
Land of Promise, The		*Samuel A. Ward*	75
Last Night		*Halfaan Kjerulf*	25
Lesson in Giving, A	Elizabeth Lincoln Gould	*C. Chaminade*	87
Life Lesson, A	Thackeray	*Schumann*	18
Lift Thine Eyes		*Mendelssohn*	96
Light-Hearted Fairy, The	Anonymous	*C. B. Edmunds*	13
Lorelei, The		*Liszt*	139

TITLE	AUTHOR	COMPOSER	PAGE
March of the Ages	M. B. Willis	*Bizet*	49
March of the Masqueraders, The		*A. S. Sullivan*	30
Midshipmite, The	F. E. Weatherly	*Stephen Adams*	108
Miss Algebra	M. B. Willis	*H. L. Heartz*	136
Morning Hymn		*J. Hatton*	58
Morning Hymn of Praise	William C. Doane	*J. Albert Jeffery*	12
My Heart Ever Faithful		*Bach*	107
My Mother	Elizabeth Lincoln Gould	*Thomas Koschat*	70
My Rose	Celia Standish	*Luigi Caracciolo*	22
Music of Autumn	M. L. Baum	*E. M. Grétry*	52
Nearer, my God, to Thee	Sarah F. Adams	*A. S. Sullivan*	134
Night	Maria Ximena Hayes	*Beethoven*	126
Old Saber, The	Louis C. Elson	*J. Offenbach*	54
Omnipresence	Oliver Wendell Holmes	*Peter Ritter*	6
Out on the Deep	Samuel K. Cowan	*Frederick N. Löhr*	140
Peace	Abbie Farwell Brown	*Beethoven*	27
Reminiscence, A		*Harvey Worthington Loomis*	52
Robert of Lincoln	William Cullen Bryant	*Henry K. Hadley*	68
Russian Lullaby	Clara Kappey	*N. Bachmetieff*	37
Russian National Anthem, The		*Alexis Lwoff*	105
Sea Gulls, The	M. A. L. Lane	*A. Alabieff*	46
Shadow-town Ferry	Lilian Dynevor Rice	*Ralph L. Baldwin*	77
Silent Night		*Fr. Gruber*	14
Slumber Song of the River	M. B. Willis	*Benjamin Godard*	103
Song of Sunshine	Elizabeth Lincoln Gould	*Benjamin Godard*	29
Song of the Waters	Nathan Haskell Dole	*Haydn*	4
Spanish Gypsy, The	M. B. Willis	*A. Saleza*	40
Spinning Maiden, The		*Hugo Jüngst*	24
Spring	Belle Ames	*Gounod*	99
Spring is Come	William Allingham	*J. M. McLaughlin*	82
Star-Spangled Banner, The	Francis Scott Key	*John Stafford Smith*	144
Stars of the Summer Night	Longfellow	*I. B. Woodbury*	9
Stories	James Montague	*M. White*	65
Summer Night, The	Elizabeth Lincoln Gould	*J. F. Nesmüller*	19
Sunset	M. L. Baum	*Schubert*	21
Sweet Rose	After Heine	*W. W. Gilchrist*	76
To Thee, O Country	Anna P. Eichberg	*Julius Eichberg*	119
To the Whippoorwill	M. B. Willis	*Elémer Szentirmay*	22
Tribute to the Soldiers	M. L. Baum	*Weber*	33
True Knight, A	M. L. Baum	*Mendelssohn*	61
Twilight at Sea	Louis C. Elson	*Rossini*	117
Victory at Saratoga, The	Abbie Farwell Brown	*Giacomo Meyerbeer*	15
Weather Vane, The	Celia Standish	*Oskar Strauss*	7
Where Would I Be?		*Karl Zöllner*	3
Whistler, The	Nixon Waterman	*G. Schleiffarth*	43
Will o' the Wisp	M. B. Willis	*A. Jungmann*	91
Wind in the Trees	Nixon Waterman	*M. Lansen*	11
Woodland Rose, The		*E. Hermes*	122